C000099830

Contract Practice
for Quantity Surveyors

Contract Practice
for Quantity Surveyors

SECOND EDITION

J. W. RAMUS ARICS

Newnes
An imprint of Butterworth-Heinemann Ltd
Linacre House, Jordan Hill, Oxford OX2 8DP

℞ A member of the Reed Elsevier plc group

OXFORD   LONDON   BOSTON
MUNICH   NEW DELHI   SINGAPORE   SYDNEY
TOKYO   TORONTO   WELLINGTON

First published 1981
Reprinted 1982
Second edition 1989
Reprinted 1990, 1991, 1993, 1994

British Library Cataloguing in Publication Data
Ramus, J. W.
Contract practice for quantity surveyors. – 2nd ed.
1. Great Britain. Buildings. Construction. Contracts
I. Title
692'.8'0941

ISBN 0 7506 0373 9

Printed and bound in Great Britain by
Biddles Ltd, Guildford and King's Lynn

Contents

Figures and tables

Preface

A number of changes in contract practice have taken place since the first edition of this book was written in 1980. Various methods of building procurement which were novel then have gained in popularity since, and others, such as Joint Venture, have appeared on the scene. Revisions to familiar standard forms of contract have been made during the decade and new ones have been published, including the ACA form and the Intermediate Contract and Management Contract forms. The basic principles of the financial management of contracts, however, still apply, even though new technology may have changed the manner in which some of them are implemented.

The book deals with the normal, straightforward discharge of quantity surveying functions but not with the more complicated aspects of professional practice, which are normally handled by experienced senior surveyors, partners or directors. Its scope has been widened somewhat by the inclusion of a chapter on extensions of time and claims for loss and expense; also one describing the non-traditional methods of building procurement referred to above.

It is hoped that the book will continue to provide a useful guide for degree students, graduates and other young surveyors with limited practical experience in quantity surveying practice and in the financial management of construction contracts. Their need is for clear, detailed, practical procedures which they can use with confidence and so be able to meet the expectations of employers and proceed capably and satisfactorily with limited supervision. It is hoped therefore that the detailed examples (which have been suitably revised and updated) will continue to meet that need.

The book will also be helpful to students preparing for the Intermediate or Final Examinations of the Royal Institution of Chartered Surveyors in the Quantity Surveying Division and those preparing for the Associate or Membership Examinations of the Chartered Institute of Building.

Although the text has been written mainly for those employed in, or expecting to be employed in, private practice or in the offices of central or local government departments, much of it is applicable to the duties of quantity surveyors in contractors' organizations and attention has been given to those duties where they differ from private practice. In the interests of conciseness, the client's quantity surveyor is hereafter referred to as 'the PQS'; where reference is made to quantity surveyors in any kind of employing organization, the term 'the surveyor' is used.

Where reference has been made to standard forms of contract, the *Standard Form of Building Contract, Private With Quantities, 1980 Edition*, with amendments, issued by the Joint Contracts Tribunal has normally been used (hereafter referred to as 'the JCT Form'). Reference has also been made to other variants of the Standard Form.

A hypothetical contract (of which details are given in Appendix A) has been used throughout to illustrate the principles discussed in the text and the interpretation of clauses in the standard forms of contract. While the text refers to the provisions of the *Standard Method of Measurement, Seventh Edition*, the bill pages used in the examples in Chapters 5 and 8 are based on SMM6 because they relate to a contract for which tenders were obtained in early 1987 (and therefore before the publication of SMM7). The differences applicable to the examples are minor.

Attention is drawn to the fact that what is described and discussed in the following chapters is related to the English law of contract and no reference is made to differences in law and practice applicable in Scotland. It is hoped nevertheless that Scottish surveyors will find much to help them in their studies and/or practice.

I wish to acknowledge with gratitude all the help and encouragement I have received in the preparation of this second edition. My thanks are due to RIBA Publications Ltd for permission to reproduce extracts from the JCT Standard Form of Building Contract, to the Royal Institution of Chartered Surveyors for permission to reproduce standard forms of valuation and to the Department of Health for allowing me to use its expenditure forecasting formula.

J. W. RAMUS

1

Contracts and the quantity surveyor

THE NATURE AND FORM OF CONTRACTS

All aspects of the quantity surveyor's professional work relate directly or indirectly to the costs of construction work of all kinds. This includes new building and civil engineering projects, and the alteration, extension or refurbishment of existing buildings. In addition, his expertise extends to consequential costs incurred by owners and occupiers after the completion of construction projects. These include repairs and redecoration, replacement of components and the operating costs of installations such as lifts, air-conditioning, heating, etc. All these costs are known collectively as 'costs-in-use' or 'life cycle costs'.

Such costs are incurred when building and engineering contractors of all kinds carry out work for clients of the construction industry. This necessarily requires that the parties concerned in a particular project enter into a contract, i.e. a legal agreement to discharge certain obligations. So, as a simple example, a builder enters into a contract with the owner of a plot of land in which he undertakes to build a house complying with the owner's requirements. On his part, the owner undertakes to pay the builder a stated sum of money.

In its simplest form a contract may be an oral agreement, the subsequent actions of the parties providing evidence of the existence of a contract. Such an agreement is legally binding, provided it does not entail an illegal act.

Alternatively, a contract may be set out in a letter or other brief document stating the essential matters agreed upon. However, such forms of contract are only suitable for the simplest projects, such as building a garage on to an existing house or erecting fencing around a plot of land. Even in those cases disputes may arise, leading to arbitration or litigation, both costly processes.

In the case of most building and engineering projects therefore it is essential that the conditions under which a contract is to be carried out and the obligations, rights and liabilities of the parties should be fully and clearly stated in writing. Even then, disputes can still arise because of ambiguity or omission in the contract documents or because something unforeseen arises during the period of the contract.

For most projects, printed standard forms are used as the basis of the contract. These set out the conditions applicable to the contract and cover all the matters which experience has shown need to be specified in order that both parties may have a clear picture of their rights and obligations.

Those matters which are peculiar to a particular project, such as names of the parties, the contract sum, commencing and completion dates, etc. are incorporated into the contract by insertion into blank spaces in the Articles of Agreement or the Appendix, both of which are part of the printed document. It is sometimes necessary for the printed text of a clause of a standard form to be amended, added to or deleted in order to accommodate particular requirements of a building owner or because the standard wording does not suit the particular circumstances of a project. Such amendments must be made with care, to avoid introducing ambiguities or inconsistencies with other clauses or other contract documents.

The National Joint Consultative Committee for Building (NJCC) has issued a Procedure Note[1] advising against extensive amendments to the JCT Form, on the grounds that such amendments may introduce inequity and that they tend away from greater standardization of building procedures. The Note also advises that when amendments are considered necessary, only a competent person should amend the Form so that ambiguities or inconsistencies which might lead to difficulties later are not introduced. This advice applies equally to all standard forms.

The advantages of using standard forms of contract instead of composing a contract document afresh for each project are:

(a) because they are written by legal experts, ambiguities and inconsistencies are reduced to a minimum;

(*b*) the rights and obligations of both parties are set out clearly and to the required degree of detail;

(*c*) because of standardization, frequent users are familiar with the provisions in a particular Form, resulting in a greater degree of consistency in their application;

(*c*) the time and expense which would otherwise be incurred in preparing a fresh document for each occasion is avoided.

The standard forms most widely used for building projects are those in the range produced by the Joint Contracts Tribunal (JCT), a body which is composed of representatives of the following organizations:

Royal Institute of British Architects
Building Employers Confederation
Royal Institution of Chartered Surveyors
Association of County Councils
Association of Metropolitan Authorities
Association of District Councils
Confederation of Associations of Specialist Engineering Contractors
Federation of Associations of Specialists and Sub-Contractors
Association of Consulting Engineers
British Property Federation
Scottish Building Contract Committee

A list of the JCT Standard Forms of Contract and Sub-Contract is given below:

1   Standard Form of Building Contract 1980 Edition (JCT 80)

(*a*) Private With Quantities.
(*b*) Private With Approximate Quantities.
(*c*) Private Without Quantities.
(*d*) Local Authorities With Quantities.
(*e*) Local Authorities With Approximate Quantities.
(*f*) Local Authorities Without Quantities.

2   Standard Form of Building Contract With Contractor Design 1981 Edition (CD 81).
3   Intermediate Form of Building Contract 1984 Edition (IFC 84).
4   Standard Form of Management Contract 1987 Edition (MC 87).

5   Fixed Fee Form of Prime Cost Contract 1967 Issue.
6   Agreement for Minor Building Works (MW 80) 1980.
7   Standard Form of Nominated Sub-Contract (NSC/4).
8   Sub-Contract Conditions to IFC 84 (NAM/SC).

In addition, there are various amendments, supplements and Practice Notes relating to JCT Forms. A complete catalogue of JCT publications is available from RIBA Publications Ltd.

Other standard forms of contract are:

(*a*) ICE Conditions of Contract (for civil engineering works, published by the Institution of Civil Engineers and the Federation of Civil Engineering Contractors).

(*b*) General Conditions of Government Contracts for Building and Civil Engineering Works (known as GC/Works/1 and published by Her Majesty's Stationery Office).

(*c*) ACA Form of Building Agreement (published by the Architectural Press Ltd for the Association of Consultant Architects).

(*d*) ACA Form of Building Agreement 1984, BPF Edition (published by the British Property Federation Ltd).

The above list is not exhaustive.

THE QUANTITY SURVEYOR'S ROLE

Many of the provisions in standard forms of contract relate to financial matters, and quantity surveyors need to have a detailed knowledge and understanding of them and be able to apply those provisions properly and in a professional manner. Consequently, most quantity surveyors have acquired considerable expertise in the use of standard forms of contract and many architects look to the quantity surveyors with whom they regularly work for advice and guidance on contractual matters. Frequently it falls to the quantity surveyor to prepare the contract documents ready for the execution of the contract by the parties, a duty which requires particular care and attention to detail.

In the performance of his duties during and after the construction period of the project, the quantity surveyor has the duty to ensure that all actions taken in relation to the financial administration of the contract will be fair to both parties.

Whilst there often is, and should be, such an attitude underlying the quantity surveyor's approach to his duties, he must not forget two important facts. First, 'fairness' is often a subjective matter so that an action or decision may be seen as fair by one person and as very unfair by another. Secondly, the surveyor's authority to act rests ultimately upon the terms of the contract and consequently, his actions must always be within the scope of those terms. Both parties to a contract, employer and contractor, are bound by the terms of that contract, having been freely agreed to by them when they signed the contract. Should any one of those terms in its practical application become disadvantageous, or even financially disastrous, to either party, the quantity surveyor has no authority to vary its provisions in order to alleviate those consequences.

The young surveyor may be tempted, by a sense of fair play which in other circumstances would be very commendable, to act in a particular situation in a way which seems to him to be fairer to one or other of the parties rather than in accordance with the strict application of the contract terms. For example, it might seem very unfair that a contractor, having complied with a verbal instruction by the architect to carry out a variation to the design of a building, should be refused payment for the extra cost just because the variation had not been confirmed in writing. The surveyor cannot do otherwise, however unfair it may seem, if the contract requires that all variations, to be valid, must be in writing.[2] Similarly, if the quantity surveyor happens to know during the construction period that either party is having cash flow problems, that knowledge must not be allowed to influence the value he puts upon work completed or unfixed materials on site when preparing a valuation for an interim certificate. However sympathetic he may feel towards either party, the surveyor must not allow his personal feelings to prevail over his judgement as to the proper application of any term of a contract. He must remember that any unwarranted advantage given to one party is likely to be at the same time an equal disadvantage to the other party. The foregoing remarks apply particularly to quantity surveyors employed in private professional firms and in the offices of local authorities, government departments, and other public bodies.

The quantity surveyor employed by a building contractor is in a somewhat different situation in that his responsibility and loyalty is primarily to his employer. Nevertheless, his actions on behalf of the contractor must equally be governed by the terms of each contract with which he deals. There is no reason, however, why the contractor's surveyor should not invoke a term of a contract to the advantage of his employer and there can be no objection to his so doing. For example, by a careful comparison of the bills of quantities and the drawings, he may be able to detect errors of omission in the quantities, the correction of which may be provided for in the contract.[3] On the other hand, he must recognize that a claim, of whatever kind, can only be justified if it is based upon a specific term of the contract and even if shown to be valid, the valuation of it may only be reached by prescribed means.[4]

But in whatever kind of organization a quantity surveyor works, his attitude to the carrying out of his duties should be a completely professional one. That is to say, the quality of the work he does should be as high as he is able to achieve, without becoming pedantic. Despite the pressures of a highly competitive business world, as a member of a respected and worthy profession, the quantity surveyor should aim to be entirely honest and impartial in his interpretation and application of the terms of a building contract, on whichever side of the contractual 'fence' he may be.

THE PQS'S POST-CONTRACT DUTIES

The following is a summary of the duties normally carried out by the PQS following acceptance of a tender for a project where an architect is responsible for the supervision and management of the contract. Some of course may not be applicable to particular projects. The respective chapters in which those duties are described in detail are given in brackets.

Before work starts on site:

1 Arrange for contract documents to be prepared ready for signatures of the parties (Chapter 6).

2 Prepare forecast of 'rate of spend' during the construction period and advise client on anticipated liability for payments on account to the contractor, giving dates and amounts (Chapter 14).

3 Make preliminary arrangements for preparing valuations for payments on account in consultation with the contractor's quantity surveyor; analyse Preliminaries and calculate amounts of time-related payments and percentage rate of cost-related payments; prepare schedule for stage payments, if applicable (Chapter 12).

During construction period:

4 Prepare valuations for payments on account at the intervals stated in the contract and agree with contractor's quantity surveyor (Chapter 12).

5 Plot payments on account on 'rate of spend' graph and report to architect on any significant divergences (Chapter 14).

6 Prepare estimates of likely cost of variations on receipt of copies of architect's instructions; later measure and value; check and price daywork vouchers (Chapter 8).

7 Advise architect, if requested, on expenditure of prime cost sums; check nominated sub-contractors' and nominated suppliers' final accounts and adjust contract sum accordingly (Chapter 7).

8 Advise architect, if requested, on expenditure of provisional sums; measure and value work carried out by the main contractor against provisional sums (except where lump sum quotations have been accepted) and adjust contract sum accordingly (Chapter 7).

9 Prepare financial reports for architect and client at the time of interim payments (Chapter 14).

10 Check main contractor's claims for increases in costs of labour, materials, levies, contributions and taxes, etc., if applicable; alternatively, apply price adjustment indices to amounts included in interim valuations (Chapter 9 and 10).

11 Measure projects based on schedules of rates or on bills of approximate quantities as the work proceeds, either on site or from architect's drawings, and value at contract rates.

12 Advise architect, if requested, on contractor's claims (if any) for loss and expense payments; if accepted, negotiate claims with contractor (Chapter 11).

After construction period:

13 Prepare final account and agree details and total with contractor's quantity surveyor (Chapter 13).

THE PQS'S LEGAL OBLIGATIONS

The PQS is normally appointed direct by the client and a contract of employment is entered into by the two of them. This may be in the form of a letter setting out the essential terms of the contract, such as the services to be provided and the basis of payment. Often the Standard Form of Agreement for the appointment of a quantity surveyor, published by the Royal Institution of Chartered Surveyors, is used.

The obligations of the PQS are governed therefore by the terms of the contract of employment. However, a person who offers professional services has a duty in law to exercise proper skill and care in the performance of those services, otherwise he may be liable for damages under the law relating to negligence. His actions are expected to be of an equal standard to those of other qualified persons practising the same profession.

Only a few cases regarding quantity surveyors have come before the courts, and the following are of particular interest.

London School Board v Northcroft Son & Neighbour (1889)

The clients brought an action against Northcrofts, the quantity surveyors, for negligence because of clerical errors in calculations which resulted in overpayments to the contractor. It was held that as the quantity surveyor had employed a skilled clerk who had carried out a large number of calculations correctly, the quantity surveyor was not liable.

Dudley Corporation v Parsons & Morris (1959)

This case centred around the interpretation of an item in a bill of quantities which stated 'extra over for excavating in rock'. It was unclear whether the item referred to the immediately preceding item of basement excavation or to all the excavation items. The seriousness of the matter from the contractor's point of view was that the item had been grossly underpriced and on remeasurement was some three times the provisional quantity in the bill. It was held by the Court of Appeal that the contractor was only entitled to be paid at the erroneous rate for the total quantity of the item as remeasured.

Tyrer v District Auditor of Monmouthshire (1974) 230 EG 973

The local authority overpaid a contractor because Tyrer, a quantity surveyor who was an employee of the authority, had accepted rates for work which he must have known were ridiculously high and had also made an arithmetical error when issuing an interim certificate. Tyrer appealed against being surcharged by the District Auditor for the loss sustained by the authority, on the grounds that he was acting in a quasi-judicial position. The appeal was rejected. The quantity surveyor owed a duty to carry out his professional work with a reasonable degree of care and skill.

Sutcliffe v Thackrah (1974) HL 1 Ll Rep 318

Although in this case the defendant was an architect, the quantity surveyor had included in two valuations the value of work which was defective, not having been advised of the defects by the architect. The client sued the architect for the cost of rectifying the defective work. The House of Lords held that the normal rules of professional negligence applied to all aspects of an architect's duties and, in exercising his functions, he must act impartially. The same obligations also apply to the actions of a quantity surveyor, although that was not a matter under consideration in this case.

REFERENCES

1. NJCC, *Procedure Note No. 2, Alterations to Standard Form of Building Contract* (London: NJCC, 1981).
2. JCT, *Standard Form of Building Contract, 1980 Edition* (London: RIBA Publications Ltd, 1988), clause 4.3.1.
3. ibid., clause 2.2.2.2.
4. ibid., clause 13.5.

2

Building procurement – traditional methods

From early in the nineteenth century until about the 1950s, the ways by which building projects were promoted and carried out in the UK conformed to straightforward and well-tried procedures. If the project was small, the building owner (or 'Employer', as he is often called) employed a building contractor to design and construct the building for him. Because buildings generally conformed to a well-defined pattern, contractors had within their organizations the full range of expertise and skills normally required.

In the case of larger projects the Employer appointed an architect to design the building, and he then produced drawings and a specification. If the architect considered it necessary (and the Employer approved), he then appointed a quantity surveyor to prepare a bill of quantities. Then, on the basis of either the specification and drawings or the bill, contractors were invited to tender in competition to carry out the work. Usually the lowest tenderer was awarded the contract.

Since the mid-1940s the architect's nomination and/or appointment of the quantity surveyor has been gradually superseded by direct appointment by the Employer, sometimes before the selection of the architect and, in some cases, the latter's selection is made on the recommendation of the quantity surveyor.

The traditional methods of building procurement are still widely used and their respective distinguishing characteristics are as described below. They have gradually evolved during the twentieth century to meet changing circumstances and technological developments, and variants of the main procedures have been introduced from time to time, but the essential principles still apply.

A. BASED ON BILLS OF FIRM QUANTITIES

The building owner commissions an architect to prepare a design and, upon virtual completion of the design, the quantity surveyor prepares a bill of quantities based upon the architect's drawings and specification information. Contractors are invited to price the bill and submit tenders in competition for carrying out the work. The contractor submitting the lowest tender is usually awarded the contract.*

The essential characteristics of this method are (i) that both the quantities and the unit rates in the bill form part of the contract and (ii) that virtual completion of the design precedes the signing of the contract. Such a contract is a *lump sum contract* (sometimes called a *fixed price contract*) because a price is stated in the contract as payment for the work described in the bill.

Advantages

1 Both parties have a clear picture of the extent of their respective commitments.

2 The unit rates in the bills provide a sound basis for the valuation of any variations to the design.

3 A detailed breakdown of the tender sum is readily available.

Disadvantages

1 The length of time taken in the design of the project and in the preparation of the bills of quantities.

2 The problem of dealing with those variations which are so fundamental or extensive as to change the character of the remainder of the work or the conditions under which it has to be carried out.

B. BASED ON BILLS OF APPROXIMATE QUANTITIES

This method is largely similar to the preceding one, except that the quantities given in the bill are approximate only and are subject to later adjustment. The essential characteristics are (i)

---

*The JCT Standard Form of Building Contract With Quantities, 1980 Edition (Private or Local Authorities version as appropriate) is commonly used.

that only the unit rates form part of the contract, and (ii) the signing of the contract and the beginning of work on site may proceed before the design is complete.

The bill of quantities is normally specially prepared for the particular project and descriptions of work are as detailed as in a bill of firm quantities, but the time otherwise required for detailed measurement of the quantities is saved, the quantities given being estimates of likely requirements. Sometimes the bill re-uses the quantities which were prepared for an earlier project of a sufficiently similar kind and size.

This method results in a contract* which is sometimes regarded as a lump sum contract although it is not strictly so, there being no total price stated in the contract. In effect, it is very similar to a schedule of rates contract (see D below).

Advantages

1   Construction on site may begin earlier.

2   The extra expense of preparing firm quantities is avoided (although this is offset by the cost of fully measuring the work as actually carried out).

Disadvantages

1   The bills of quantities cannot be relied upon as giving a realistic total cost at tender stage and in consequence, the parties to the contract are less certain of the extent of their commitment.

2   The construction works have to be measured completely as actually carried out, which may prove more costly than to have prepared bills of firm quantities initially.

3   The architect may feel less pressure to make design decisions which ought to be taken at an early stage.

C. BASED ON DRAWINGS AND SPECIFICATION

This method closely resembles that described in A above, the difference being that no bills of quantities are supplied to ten-

---

*The JCT Standard Form of Building Contract With Approximate Quantities 1980 Edition (Private or Local Authorities version as appropriate) is commonly used.

derers, who have to prepare their own quantities from the drawings provided. This procedure is intended to be used for relatively small works (say, not exceeding £50,000) and for sub-contract works, although it is not unknown for quite large contracts to be tendered for on this basis. A survey carried out by the Junior Organization of the RICS showed that the average value of contracts let on this basis during 1987 was just under £200,000.[1]

The essential characteristics are (i) that tenderers are supplied only with complete working drawings and a full specification, and (ii) that virtual completion of the design must precede the signing of the contract.*

Advantages

1 The time required for the preparation of tender documents is reduced, as the time-consuming process of preparing bills of quantities is eliminated.

2 Both parties can have a clear picture of their respective commitments at the time of signing the contract.

Disadvantages

1 No breakdown of the tender sum is immediately available (although the tenderers may be asked to provide a Contract Sum Analysis, either as a part of their tender submission or subsequently).

2 The valuation of variations presents problems, as indicated above.

3 There is little, if any, control over the percentage rates for additions for overheads and profit to the prime cost of labour, materials and plant elements in dayworks (defined on p. 106). Tenderers are normally asked to state percentage rates to be used in the event of dayworks arising. Where such rates have no effect on the tender sum, there is little incentive to the tenderer to moderate them.

*The JCT Standard Form of Building Contract Without Quantities, 1980 Edition (Private or Local Authorities version as appropriate) is commonly used.

D. BASED ON A SCHEDULE OF RATES (sometimes known as *measured contracts* or *measurement contracts*)

This method operates in a similar way to that described in B. above, tenders being based upon a schedule of rates as explained in (i)–(iii) below. A particular advantage arising from its use is that it allows for a contract to be signed and work to start on site when the design is only in outline form, and in consequence the pre-contract period is reduced considerably.

(i) Standard schedule

A standard schedule lists under appropriate trade headings all the items likely to arise in any construction project, with a unit rate against each item. The best-known of such schedules is the *Schedule of Rates for Building Works* prepared by the Property Services Agency of the Department of the Environment.[2]

Tenderers are asked to tender percentage additions (or deductions) to the listed rates, usually by sections or sub-sections, thus allowing for variations in construction costs since the date of the preparation of the schedule used.

Advantage

1   Tenderers using a particular schedule often soon become familiar both with the item descriptions and the rates and are able to assess percentage adjustments relatively easily.

Disadvantages

1   In comparing and assessing a range of tenders, the PQS has the task of gauging the effect of a series of variables, making the choice of the most favourable tender difficult.

2   The parties are unable to have a precise indication of their respective commitments.

(ii) 'Ad hoc' schedule

This is a schedule specially prepared for a particular project and lists only those items which are appropriate to that project, including any special or unusual items. An *'ad hoc'* schedule may be pre-priced by the PQS (in which case the form of the tender will be the same as when using a standard schedule) or the rate column may be left blank by the PQS for the tenderer to insert individual rates against each item. The latter method, because of the absence of quantities, makes the comparison and assessment of tenders much more difficult.

Advantages

1 Tenderers are only required to concern themselves with a restricted range of items, thus enabling them to assess rates or percentages more accurately.

2 Tenderers are able to obtain a clearer picture of the scope of the work from the items listed in the schedule.

Disadvantages

These are similar to those applying to standard schedules.

(iii) Bills of quantities from previous contract

The bill of quantities used will normally be for a comparable type of building of similar constructional form to the proposed project. It is, in effect, a pre-priced *'ad hoc'* schedule and will be used in the same way.

This is the method of tendering normally used in *serial tendering*, described on p. 46.

Advantages

1 The time required to prepare tender documents is reduced to the minimum.

2 Tenderers have to consider only a restricted range of items.

Disadvantages

1 The parties are unable to have a precise indication of their respective commitments.

2 There may be a considerable discrepancy between the successful tender and the real cost of the work, owing to the approximate nature of the quantities.

E. BASED ON COST REIMBURSEMENT (also known as
prime cost or *cost plus* because the method of payment is by
reimbursement to the contractor of his prime cost, plus a management fee)

There are three variants of this type of contract, distinguished by
the way in which the fee is calculated. Each is dealt with
separately below.*

'Prime cost' means the total cost to the contractor of buying
materials, goods and components, of using or hiring plant and of
employing labour, in order to carry out construction works.

Of all the types of contract, this produces the most uncertainty
as to the financial outcome. Tenders contain no total sum and it
may be very difficult to form any reliable estimate of the final cost.

It is widely recognized as the most uneconomical type of
contract and therefore is one which normally should be used only
in circumstances where none of the other types is appropriate.
Because of the possibility of inefficiency and waste of resources,
contracts of this type need to embody provisions giving the
architect some control over the level of labour and plant employed.

One of the attractions of prime cost contracts is that work on site
can commence in the early stages of design and this may be all-
important to the client. There may be circumstances where, to
him, cost is a less important factor than time. Consequently, a
start on site at the earliest possible time may be financially more
advantageous in the long run than a lower final cost of construction which might have resulted from the use of another type of
contract.

It should be noted that no site measuring is necessary other
than as checks on the quantities of materials for which the
contractor submits invoices, and for purposes of checking nominated sub-contractors' and nominated suppliers' accounts.

The process of calculating and verifying the total prime cost
involves a vast amount of investigation and checking of invoices,
time sheets, sub-contractors' accounts, etc., which can be both
tedious and time-consuming. It is therefore in the interests of both
the PQS and the contractor that at the outset a proper system of
recording, verifying and valuing the prime cost is agreed and
strictly implemented. In addition, it is vitally important to define

*The only standard form available for this type of contract is the JCT
Fixed Fee Form of Prime Cost Contract (*see* Section (ii) on p. 18).

clearly what is intended to be included as prime cost and what is intended to be covered by the fee. The standard form for the fixed fee variant of this type of contract does so in the appended schedules.[3] The publication *Definition of prime cost of daywork*[4] may be adapted for this purpose if the standard form is not used.

The advantages and disadvantages of prime cost contracts over lump sum and schedule of rates contracts follow.

Advantages

1 The time required for preparation of tender documents and for obtaining tenders is minimized, thus enabling an early start on site to be made.

2 Work on site may proceed before the detailed design is complete.

Disadvantages

1 The parties have the least precise indication of their respective commitments.

2 The cost of construction to the client is likely to be greater than if other types of contract were to be used.

3 The computation and verification of the total prime cost is a long and tedious process.

The variants below differ in the way in which the fee for the contractor's services is determined. Variants (ii) and (iii) are the consequence of a general acknowledgement that it is desirable to provide an incentive to economize in the use of resources on the part of the contractor.

(i) Cost plus percentage fee

The contractor is paid a fee equal to an agreed percentage of the prime costs of labour, materials and plant used in carrying out the work.

The outstanding disadvantage (to the client) is that the more inefficient the contractor's operations are and the greater the waste of resources, the higher the fee paid to the contractor will be. (To counter this, the percentage is sometimes made to vary inversely as the prime cost.)

The following is a simple illustration of this contractual arrangement, which at the same time will provide a basis for comparison with the fixed fee form. A contract is assumed where the *estimated* total cost of materials, labour, and plant was £50,000; the contractor's overheads were calculated by him as 15 per cent and he required 5 per cent for profit. He therefore tendered at 20 per cent overall addition to the prime cost as his fee and his tender was accepted. Assuming that the estimate of prime cost proved at the completion of the contract to be accurate, the total final cost to the client would be:

	£		£
Total prime cost			50 000
15% addition for overheads	7500	20%	10 000
5% addition for profit	2500		
Total cost of contract			60 000

If, however, due to uneconomic organization of the contract, inefficiency and excessive waste, the total prime cost was £55,000 for the same job, then the total cost would be:

	£
Total prime cost	55 000
20% addition for overheads and profit	11 000
Total cost of contract	66 000

As the contractor's overheads chargeable to this job would still be £7500, it follows that the real profit would be £3500. The disincentive to the contractor to work efficiently is thus seen to be strong.

(ii) Cost plus fixed fee

Under this variant, the fee paid to the contractor is a fixed sum which normally does not vary with the total prime cost, but is based on an estimate of the likely total. The only ground on which the fee might be varied is if either the scope of the work or the conditions of carrying it out were to be materially altered after the contractor tendered.

It should be noted that the fee, if considered in percentage terms, is lower when the prime cost is higher.

Using the same illustration as before, but with the contractor having tendered a fixed fee of £10,000 (made up of £7500 for overheads and £2500 for profit), the sum paid to the contractor as fee would be equivalent to 20 per cent if the total prime cost was £50,000.

If as before, the prime cost was higher for the same reasons, the financial picture would be:

	£	£
Total prime cost		55 000
Overheads	7500	
Profit	2500	10 000
Total cost of contract		65 000

The fee is now equal to 18.18 per cent of the prime cost and the profit portion only 4.55 per cent. If the prime cost rose to £60,000, the fee would equal only 16.67 per cent and the profit portion 4.17 per cent.

(iii) Target cost

This variant is really one or other of the two preceding ones with another factor added. As an incentive to reducing the total prime cost, the agreement provides for a bonus to be paid to the contractor if the total cost is less than an agreed sum (the 'target') and also a penalty to be paid by him if the total cost exceeds that sum. The bonus and penalty are commonly 50 per cent of the difference between the total amounts, but may be any agreed percentages. The target cost is an estimate of the likely total cost.

Taking the same illustration again, it is assumed that the fixed fee method of payment is to be used, and that the agreed sum based on an estimate of likely total cost is £60,000. At the end of the job, (assuming the higher cost shown above), the final payment would be calculated like this:

	£
Total prime cost	55 000
Fixed fee	10 000
	65 000
Deduct penalty, being 50% of excess over £60 000	2 500
Amount of final payment	62 500

In effect, the fee has been reduced to £7500, which is only just enough to meet overheads, leaving nothing for profit. It follows therefore that the contractor will need to be very satisfied that the 'agreed sum' is a realistic estimate of likely cost and the PQS must give him every reasonable opportunity and assistance to satisfy himself in that regard.

However, if the contractor were able to reduce the prime cost, say to £48,000, final payment would be calculated as:

	£
Total prime cost	48 000
Fixed fee	10 000
	58 000
Add bonus, being 50% of saving over £60 000	1 000
Amount of final payment	59 000

The fee has now increased to £11,000, including £3500 for profit, the overheads remaining at £7500. As a percentage, the profit is 7.29 per cent of the prime cost. Thus, under this contractual arrangement, an extra cost or saving is shared between the client and the contractor.

THE COMPOSITE NATURE OF CONTRACTS

Although, for convenience, classifications and type labels such as the foregoing are commonly used, in practice contracts often combine the characteristics of two or more types. McCanlis has pointed out[5] that, for example, a lump sum contract based on bills of firm quantities, often contains items with provisional quantities requiring remeasurement and therefore such items bear the characteristics of a schedule of rates contract. Also, the provisional sums included in the bills for daywork and expended on work which is not readily measurable or not reasonably priceable as measured work, form a prime cost plus percentage fee contract within the main lump sum contract. Thus, many contracts which are regarded as of the lump sum type are, in reality, a combination of several types. Other examples of the composite nature of many contracts are given in the reference above.

CIRCUMSTANCES IN WHICH THE VARIOUS TYPES OF CONTRACT MAY BE USED

Usually the circumstances peculiar to a project will indicate which type of contract is most appropriate. Occasionally, more than one type might be suitable, in which case, the one which seems to offer the greatest benefits to the client should be chosen as he is the one who will be paying the bill.

The suitability of the types of contract discussed earlier may be related to varying circumstances as follows.

Based on firm bills of quantities

(i) When there is time to prepare a sufficiently complete design to enable accurate quantities to be measured.

(ii) When the client's total commitment must be known beforehand, for example, in order to make adequate borrowing arrangements or when approval to the proposed expenditure has to be obtained from a finance or housing committee of a local authority, from a central government department or from a board of directors.

Based on bills of approximate quantities

(i) When the design is fairly well advanced but there is insufficient time to take off accurate quantities or the design will not be sufficiently complete soon enough for that to be done.

(ii) When it is desired to have the advantages of detailed bills but without the cost in terms of time and/or money.

Based on drawings and specification

(i) When the project is fairly small, i.e. up to a value of, say, £50,000.

(ii) Where time is short and the client considers it to be less important to have the benefits of bills of quantities than the early completion of the construction work, while retaining the advantages of a lump sum contract.

Based on a schedule of rates

(i) When the details of the design have not yet been worked out or there is considerable uncertainty in regard to them.

(ii) When time is pressing.

(iii) When *term contracts* are envisaged. These are appropriate where a limited range of repetitive work is required to be carried out, such as the external redecoration of an estate of houses. The contractor tenders on the basis of unit rates, which are to remain current for the stated 'term', usually one year or the estimated period which the proposed work will take.

Based on prime cost plus fee

(i) When time is short and cost is not as important as time.

(ii) When the client wishes to use a contractor who has worked satisfactorily for him before and whom he can trust to operate efficiently, while being prepared to pay the higher cost entailed in return for the advantages.

(iii) In cases of emergency, such as repairs to dangerous structures.

(iv) For maintenance contracts.

(v) For alterations jobs where there is insufficient time or it is impracticable to produce the necessary documentation.

The following examples will illustrate some of the foregoing considerations.

Example 1

A client company owned a department store in a prime position in Manchester. It had acquired the adjoining site for an extension which it was estimated would cost £500,000. The Board of Directors wanted the work to be done by a particular contractor who had done work for them before.

Apart from the choice of the contractor, the important consideration from the client's point of view was the need to commence trading in the new extension at the earliest possible date and also to restrict the disturbance to their normal trading operations to as short a period as possible.

Of the variants to the lump sum type of contract, only the drawings and specification type could be considered on the ground of time but because of the early start requirement it was rejected. As it was thought unlikely that there would be many variations during the course of construction, the schedule of rates type was rejected too.

The clients were not so concerned about cost as about time, and because they knew the contractors and were satisfied that they would do an efficient and speedy job, the type of contract eventually recommended (and used) was the target cost form of prime cost plus a fixed fee. The contractors produced an estimate of cost of £530,000 and after some negotiation the target cost was finally agreed at £518,000.

Example 2

The clients were manufacturers of clothing and had a new factory in the early stages of construction in a suburb of Birmingham. The contract was based on bills of quantities and the work was proceeding on schedule. Another site had been acquired by the clients for a building of similar size and form of construction about 18 miles away at Coventry. The clients were anxious to begin production as soon as possible in both factories.

As the two sites were reasonably close and time was an important factor, the type of contract based on a pre-priced schedule of rates (namely, the priced bills of quantities for the first contract) seemed the best choice. The prices in those bills could only be used, of course, if the same contractor were able and willing to take on the second contract as he held the copyright in the prices. In the event, he was prepared to do so and percentage additions to each of the work sections in the bills were negotiated between the PQS and the contractor's estimator. A new 'Preliminaries' section of the bills appropriate to the second project was prepared and prices negotiated for the items in it.

Example 3

An Inner London Borough Council was proposing to improve some 1500 of its older dwellings by replacing all the sanitary appliances with modern equipment over the next three or four years. Finance had already been allocated for the work to commence in the current financial year and a start was to be made as soon as contracts could be arranged.

The main characteristic of this situation was the large amount of repetition of relatively few items of work. Time was also a factor in so far that an early start was essential if allocated finance during the current financial year was to be fully used.

The circumstances all pointed to 'term contracts', and, accordingly, contracts based on *ad hoc* schedules were used. Schedules of the plumbing and associated builder's work items were drawn up for tenderers to insert their own rates against the items. Provision was made in the contracts for the rates to be updated at 12-monthly intervals.

THE RISK FACTOR

An important element of construction contracting is risk, i.e. the risk the parties take that the implementation of the contract may be detrimental in some degree to their financial or other interests. On his part, the contractor takes the risk that his anticipated profit will be reduced or converted into a loss as a result of the outworking of the conditions under which the contract is carried out. On his part, the Employer takes the risk that he will become liable for a greater total cost than he envisaged when initiating the project.

The types of contract described above carry a varying degree of risk for the parties. Generally speaking, the contractor's risk increases as the Employer's risk reduces and *vice versa*. Thus, the contractor bears a high degree of risk where the contract is based on drawings and specification only, for two reasons. First, as it is a lump sum contract, he must estimate his expected costs as accurately as possible because any adverse mistake will reduce his profit. Secondly, there being no bill of quantities provided for tendering purposes, he must take off his own quantities from the drawings in order to formulate his tender, and, again, any error he may make in the process will affect his profit margin.

The Employer's risk is small in the situation just described. He knows at the outset what his financial liability will be and is under no contractual obligation to reimburse the contractor for any errors which he may have made in preparing his tender.

At the other end of the spectrum, where a cost reimbursement contract is used, the contractor's risk is reduced considerably because he is paid his full costs and a fee in addition. His only risk is in pitching at the right level the fee which he tenders but, even so, he is most unlikely to make a loss. On his part, however, the Employer bears the risk of the prime cost becoming much higher than estimated, owing perhaps to an inefficient site agent or to wastage of resources.

Other types of contract fall within these two extremes and Figure 1 indicates a ranking of them according to the allocation of risk borne by the parties.

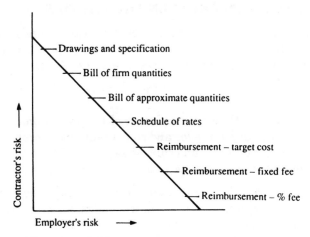

Figure 1   Allocation of risk

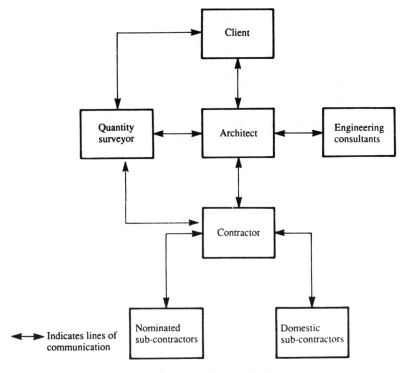

Figure 2   Relationships and communication links

RELATIONSHIPS BETWEEN THE PARTIES

In all the traditional types of contract, the pattern of relationships between all the parties is normally similar. Figure 2 illustrates these relationships and indicates the lines of communication between them.

Contractual links exist:

(i) between the Employer and each of his professional advisers (architect, quantity surveyor and consultant engineers);
(ii) between Employer and contractor;
(iii) between the contractor and each sub-contractor.

There may also be Warranty Agreements between the Employer and sub-contractor if the Employer wishes (as, for example, by use of Forms NSC/2 or NSC/2a in conjunction with JCT 80).

REFERENCES

1. RICS, Contracts in Use, *Chartered Quantity Surveyor*, 1989, Vol. 11, No. 5, p. 24.
2. *Schedule of Rates for Building Works, 1985* (London: HMSO, 1985).
3. *Fixed Fee form of Prime Cost Contract for building works, 1967 issue* (London: RIBA Publications Ltd, 1976).
4. *Definition of prime cost of daywork carried out under a building contract* (London: Royal Institution of Chartered Surveyors, 1975).
5. McCANLIS, E. W., *Tendering Procedures and Contractual Arrangements* (London: Royal Institution of Chartered Surveyors, 1967), p. 10.

3
Building procurement – alternative methods

Since the early 1960s, various alternative ways of promoting and carrying out construction projects have been devised with varying degrees of success. The reasons why many building owners and developers considered that the traditional procedures were no longer satisfactory were:

(i) The rapidly spiralling cost of construction meant that large sums of money had to be borrowed to finance projects;

(ii) high interest rates meant that the time occupied by the traditional procedures resulted in substantial additions to the construction cost;

(iii) clients were becoming more knowledgeable on construction matters and were demanding better value for money and an earlier return on their investment;

(iv) high technology installations required a higher quality of construction.

Attention has focused on reducing the time traditionally occupied in producing a design and preparing tender documentation, thus enabling construction work to begin sooner.

Another important factor has been bringing the contractor in at an early stage in the design of a project. Under the traditional procedures, the contractor rarely played any part until the tender stage was reached, after virtual completion of the design. The increasing complexity of projects, however, led to the realization that it was in the interests of clients and architects to use the vast amount of knowledge and practical experience of contractors early in the design process, and that this would make a valuable contribution to a successful outcome.

The following are the principal alternative methods of building procurement now in use.

A. DESIGN AND BUILD (sometimes called *design and construct* or *package deals*)

When first introduced in its modern form, this method usually meant the contractor using an industrialized building system which was adapted to meet the client's requirements – usually straightforward, rectangular warehouse or factory buildings with a minimum of design. More recently, the method has been applied to a wide range of building types.

Essentially the contractor is responsible for the design, for the planning, organization and control of the construction and for generally satisfying the client's requirements, and offers his service for an inclusive sum. A proprietary, prefabricated building system may or may not be used.

The procedure is initiated by the client (or an architect on his behalf) preparing his requirements in as much or as little detail as he thinks fit. These are then sent to a selection of suitable contractors, each of whom prepares his proposals on design, time and cost, which he submits together with an analysis of his tender sum. The client then accepts the proposals he is satisfied best meet his requirements and enters into a contract* with the successful tenderer. The latter then proceeds to develop his design proposals and to carry out and complete the works.

The client may use the services of an independent architect and quantity surveyor to advise him on the contractor's proposals as to design and construction methods and as to the financial aspects respectively. He may also appoint an agent to supervise the works and generally to act on his behalf to ensure that the contractor's proposals are complied with.

Figure 3 shows the normal pattern of relationships and indicates the lines of communication between the parties in a design and build contract.

Contractual links exist:

*The JCT Standard Form of Building Contract With Contractor's Design 1981 Edition is a suitable form of contract.

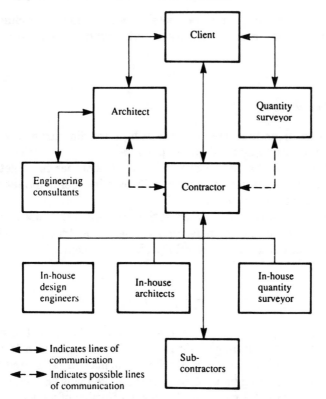

Figure 3 Design and build contracts: relationships of the parties

(i) between the client and the contractor;
(ii) between the contractor and each sub-contractor;
(iii) between the client and each of his independent advisers.

Advantages

1 Single point responsibility is provided, i.e. the contractor is solely responsible for failure in the design and/or the construction.

2 The client has only one person to deal with, namely, the contractor, whose design team includes architects, quantity surveyors, structural engineers, etc.

3 The client is aware of his total financial commitment from the outset.

4 Close intercommunication between the contractor's design

and construction teams promotes co-operation in achieving smoother running of the contract and prompt resolution of site problems.

Disadvantages

1 Variations from the original design are discouraged by the contractor and, if allowed, are expensive.

2 The client has no means of knowing whether he is getting value for money unless he employs his own independent advisers, which adds to his costs.

3 If the contractor's organization is relatively small, he is unlikely to be as expert on design as he is on construction, and the resulting building may be aesthetically less acceptable.

B. MANAGEMENT CONTRACTING

This method has been increasing in popularity since the early 1970s. A study of management contracting carried out in 1985 by the Centre for Construction Market Information estimated that the output of management contracting in 1984 was £890m, with a growth in 1985 of 9 per cent. A survey of usage of various forms and types of contract carried out in 1988[1] showed that management contracts were used on 9.41 per cent of projects (by total value) in 1987 compared with 14.4 per cent in 1985 and 12.01 per cent in 1984.

The principal characteristic of management contracting is that the management contractor does none of the construction work himself but it is divided up into work packages which are sub-let to sub-contractors, each of whom enters into a contract with the management contractor. The latter is normally either nominated by the client on the basis of the contractor's previous experience of management contracting or is selected by competition based upon tenders obtained from a number of suitable contractors for (a) the management fees and (b) prices for any additional services to be provided before or during the construction period (unless to be paid for on a prime cost basis, in which case the tenders will include percentage additions required to the respective categories

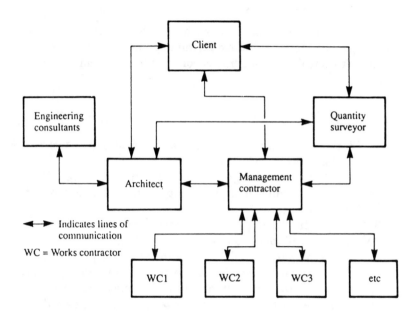

Figure 4   Management contracts: relationships of the parties

of prime cost). The successful contractor will then enter into a contract* with the client.

The management contractor's role therefore is that of providing a construction management service on a fee basis as part of the client's management team – organizing, co-ordinating, supervising and managing the construction works in co-operation with the client's other professional consultants. As part of his service, he provides and maintains all the necessary site facilities, such as offices, storage and mess huts, power supplies and other site services, common construction plant, welfare, essential attendances on the works contractors (e.g. unloading and storing materials, providing temporary roads and hardstandings and removing rubbish and debris) and dealing with labour relations matters.

Figure 4 shows the usual pattern of relationships and indicates the lines of communication between the parties to a management contract.

*The JCT Standard Form of Management Contract 1987 Edition is a suitable form of contract.

Contractual links exist:

(i) between the client and each member of the design and management team (including the management contractor);
(ii) between the management contractor and each of the sub-contractors.

Advantages

1 Work can begin on site as soon as the first one or two works packages have been designed.

2 Overlapping of design and construction can significantly reduce the time requirement, resulting in an earlier return on the client's investment.

3 The contractor's practical knowledge and management expertise are available to assist the design team.

4 Where the nature and extent of the work may be uncertain, as in refurbishment contracts, the design of later work packages may be delayed until more information becomes available as the work progresses, without extending the construction period.

5 The contractor, being part of the client's team, is able to identify with the client's needs and interests.

6 Because works contracts are entered into close to the time of their commencement on site, they can be based on firm price tenders.

Disadvantages

1 Uncertainty as to the final cost of the project until the last works contract has been signed.

2 The number of variations and the amount of remeasurement required may be greater than on traditional contracts because of the greater opportunity to make changes in design during the construction period, because of problems connected with the interface between packages, and because packages are sometimes let on less than complete design information.

C. BRITISH PROPERTY FEDERATION (BPF) SYSTEM

This system was introduced at the end of 1983 by the British Property Federation, which represents property, development, insurance and financial organizations who are the customers of the construction industry. It published a *Manual* at that time describing the system in detail, and in 1984 published the BPF Edition of the ACA Form of Building Agreement.*

The System claims 'to produce good buildings more quickly and at lower cost' and 'to remove as much as possible of the overlap of effort between designers, quantity surveyors and contractors'. It operates by a progression through five stages, as follows:

Stage 1 – *Concept*: during which the client produces an outline brief and appoints a client's representative.

Stage 2 – *Preparation of the brief*: during which a design leader is appointed to prepare a design programme and the client's representative develops the brief containing a cost plan, time limits and basic design requirements; he also sets a target cost.

Stage 3 – *Design development*: during which the design leader expands the brief into drawings and a specification.

Stage 4 – *Tender documentation and tendering*: during which tender documents (drawings, a time schedule and a schedule of activities or bills of quantities) are produced and competitive tenders obtained.

Stage 5 – *Construction*: during which the client's representative has responsibility for all aspects of management, a supervisor monitors the works on behalf of the client, and a site manager is the full-time representative of the contractor on site.

The BPF System therefore broadly follows the traditional procurement pattern but is different in the following respects:

(i) the client's representative, who is named in the contract, is in control in the role of project manager, no architect, as such, being named in the contract;

(ii) the client's representative (unlike the architect under JCT contracts) may delegate any or all of his duties to any number of persons or firms;

(iii) a priced schedule of activities may replace the traditional bill of quantities, with the intention of reducing the length of time (and therefore cost to the client) necessary for preparing contract documents;

*The JCT Standard Form of Building Contract With Contractor's Design 1981 Edition (with 1987 amendments) is a suitable alternative form of contract.

(iv) a proportion of the design work is transferred to the contractor, the amount depending upon the extent of design included in the tender documents;

(v) variations, it is claimed, are reduced to a minimum, by all concerned being encouraged to make prompt decisions;

(vi) there is no provision for nominated sub-contractors or nominated suppliers but certain work or certain goods may be stipulated as to be carried out or to be supplied by a person or one of a list of persons named in the contract documents;

(vii) the design leader and other consultants are paid a lump sum fee instead of a percentage of the value of the project;

(viii) disputes are settled by a named adjudicator in order to speed up settlement, with arbitration in reserve if the parties are not satisfied with his decisions and for those matters not specified in the contract as referable to the adjudicator.

Figure 5 shows the pattern of relationships between the parties in a contract using the BPF System and indicates the lines of communication between them.

Contractual links exist:

(i) between the client and the client's representative;
(ii) between the client and the design leader;
(iii) between the client and each design consultant;
(iv) between the client and the supervisor;
(v) between the client and the contractor.

Advantages

1 Some or most of the design work may be transferred to the contractor, thereby obtaining the benefits of his expertise and also shortening the pre-contract period.

2 All those working on a project are aware of their respective duties and responsibilities, as they are clearly defined in detail in the BPF Manual.

3 The matters to be specified or shown in the brief, the master cost plan and in the tender documents are fully detailed in the Appendixes to the Manual.

4 The prescribed management structure is calculated to induce a greater sense of urgency in the minds of the consultants, and the system is designed to reduce as far as possible the total project period.

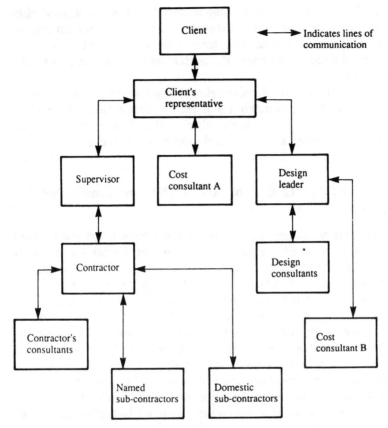

Figure 5 BPF contracts: relationships of the parties

Disadvantages

1   Where a bill of quantities is not provided by the client, the scope of the work covered by the contractor's price is less precisely defined.

2   If a bill of quantities is not provided, errors of omission by a successful tenderer inevitably lead to claims and/or to cutting corners in an attempt to recover the consequential loss.

3   The pricing of variations will lead to more protracted negotiations between the client's representative and the contractor where a bill of quantities is not used.

4   Some contractors may not be sufficiently competent in interpreting and developing designs from conceptual information.

5   The use of one contractor in the design process inevitably brings in also those sub-contractors with whom that contractor normally works, which may leave the client in the position of feeling obliged to use those subcontractors subsequently without competition.

6   The dominant role of the client's representative could lead to contractors being somewhat less than satisfied that they will be treated with the same impartiality as they have come to expect from independent architects and quantity surveyors.

D. CONSTRUCTION MANAGEMENT (sometimes called the *separate contracts system*)

Construction management is not a procurement system in itself but is only part of the total process. It is a professional consultant service to the client, provided on a fee basis, with the design and construction services being provided by other organizations.

The construction manager is responsible for the organization and planning of the construction work on site and for arranging for it to be carried out in the most efficient manner. The construction work itself is normally carried out by a number of contractors, each of whom is responsible for a defined work package. All the work packages together constitute the total project. Each works contractor enters into a direct contract with the client.

The construction manager's duties normally include any or all of the following:

(i) co-operation and consultation with the other members of the client's professional team;

(ii) preparation and updating of a detailed construction programme;

(iii) preparation of materials and components flows and arranging for advance ordering;

(iv) determining what site facilities and services are required and their location;

(v) breaking down the project into suitable work packages in consultation with the other members of the client's team and recommending suitable contractors to be invited to tender for work packages;

(vi) obtaining tenders from contractors and suppliers;

(vii) evaluating tenders and making recommendations on them to the client's team;

(viii) co-ordinating the work of the works contractors to ensure that it is carried out in accordance with the master programme;

(ix) establishing all necessary management personnel on site with responsibility to manage and supervise the project;

(x) dealing with any necessary variations to the work, providing the design manager with estimates of their likely cost and subsequently issuing instructions to works contractors;

(xi) submitting to the quantity surveyor applications from works contractors for periodic payments and all necessary documentation enabling the final accounts of works contractors to be settled.

Figure 6 shows the normal pattern of relationships between the parties and indicates the lines of communication between them.

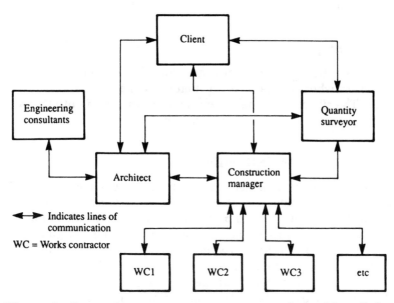

Figure 6 Construction management contracts: relationships of the parties. *Note*: Lines of communication also exist between the architect and quantity surveyor and each of the works contractors. To avoid confusion, these lines are omitted

Contractual links exist:

(i) between the client and the construction manager;
(ii) between the client and each of the works contractors;
(iii) between the client and each of his professional advisers (architect, quantity surveyor, engineering consultants, etc.).

Advantages

1 The construction work is more closely integrated into the management of the project.

2 Close liaison between the construction manager and design manager leads to prompt identification of and decisions relating to practical problems.

3 Detailed design can continue in parallel with construction, work packages being let in succession as the design of each is completed, thus shortening the project time.

4 Privity of contract between the client and each of the works contractors provides the client with a readier means of redress in the event of difficulties, such as delays, arising.

Disadvantages

1 The client has one more consultant and a number of contractors with whom to deal instead of only one main contractor.

2 The client's financial commitment is uncertain until the last of the works contracts has been signed.

E. PROJECT MANAGEMENT

Project Management is not a procurement system in itself, in that it does not include the site construction process but only its general supervision. It has been defined[2] as 'the overall planning, control and co-ordination of a project from inception to completion aimed at meeting a client's requirements and ensuring completion on time, within cost and to required quality standards'.

A number of project management organizations came into existence during the late 1970s and 1980s to meet the need for the management of projects which were becoming larger and increasingly complex. Many clients do not have the in-house skills and experience necessary for the successful management of construction projects and so need to employ an independent project management company to do it for them.

Quantity surveyors, by their training and experience in financial and contractual matters, coupled with a detailed knowledge of construction processes, are well qualified to offer a project management service, and a number of established quantity surveying practices have set up associated companies offering such a service. Other groups of professionals, such as architects, engineers and building and valuation surveyors, are also now filling this role.

The project manager, in effect, becomes the client's representative, with authority to supervise and control the entire planning and building operation from acquisition of the site to completion of the project and settlement of the accounts. The service he provides is essentially one of planning, organizing and co-ordinating the services provided by surveyors and lawyers in relation to site acquisition; the architect, engineers and quantity surveyor in relation to project planning and design; and the contractor and sub-contractors in carrying out the site construction work; but does not include the carrying out of any of their duties himself.

Figure 7 shows the normal pattern of relationships between the parties and indicates the lines of communication between them. Contractual links exist:

(i) between client and project manager;
(ii) between client and each of his professional advisers;
(iii) between client and contractor;
(iv) between contractor and each sub-contractor.

F. JOINT VENTURE

This is an arrangement for building procurement which has developed out of the increasing complexity of construction projects, often with unorthodox methods or sequences of construction. It is applicable to large-scale projects of, say, £5m value or more, where there is a higher than normal proportion of engineering and other specialist services. It has been defined as follows:

A partnership between two or more companies covering building, mechanical and electrical engineering, or other specialist services for the purpose of tendering for, and executing a building or civil engineering contract, each of the participating

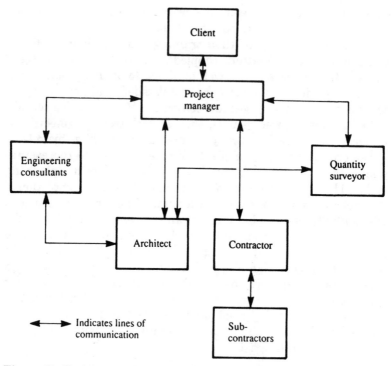

Figure 7 Project management: relationships of the parties

companies having joint and several liability for their contractual obligations to the employer.[3]

The basis of such projects is a single contract to which all the partner companies to the joint venture are signatories. Any of the standard forms of contract in current use may form the contract document, and in the publication just quoted the NJCC recommends the use of JCT 80 for projects not primarily of an engineering nature. Modifications will need to be made to cover joint and several liability of the participating companies and to provide for any performance warranty which the Employer may require.

Joint venture has the effect of making specialist contractors who under more orthodox arrangements would be sub-contractors, partners with the building contractor. This does not preclude the use of sub-contractors (whether nominated, named or listed), a role which is filled by secondary specialist contractors who are not partners in the joint venture.

Advantages

1 The combined resources of participating companies result in greater economy in the use of specialist manpower, design and equipment.

2 There is a greater degree of unified action between the contracting parties.

3 Lines of communication between the Employer's professional advisers and the building contractor and specialist contractors are shorter and better-defined.

4 Improved integration of work sequences results in a shorter contract time and fewer management problems.

Disadvantages

1 If one JV partner withdraws, the remaining partner or partners must accept total liability to complete the project.

2 A separate, unified JV bank account must be arranged and maintained by all the partners.

3 Separate insurance policies must be taken out on behalf of all the JV partners, specifically for the proposed project.

4 A board of management with a single managing director needs to be appointed jointly by the JV partners to ensure unified actions.

The pattern of relationships in a Joint Venture project and the lines of communication between the parties are similar to those illustrated in Figure 2, but with the JV partners together fulfilling the role of 'Contractor'.

Contractual links exist:

(i) between the JV participating companies;

(ii) between the Employer and the JV partners collectively;

(iii) between the Employer and each of his professional advisers;

(iv) between the JV partners and each of the sub-contractors.

REFERENCES

1. RICS, Contracts in Use, *Chartered Quantity Surveyor* 1989, Vol. 11, No. 5, p. 24.

2. RICS, Project Management: Defining the Terms, *Chartered Quantity Surveyor* 1986, Vol. 8, No. 11, p. 20.

3. NJCC, *Guidance Note 1 – Joint Venture Tendering for Contracts in the UK* (London: RIBA Publications Ltd, 1985), p. 1.

4

Tendering methods and procedures

METHODS OF CONTRACTOR SELECTION

The selection of a contractor to carry out a construction project is an important matter requiring careful thought. A wrong choice may lead to an unhappy client/contractor relationship, a dissatisfied client and possibly even an insolvent contractor.

Any one contractor will not be suitable for any one job. A contracting organization will be geared to work of a particular size or price range and will be unsuitable or uneconomic for contracts outside that range. For example, a national company would probably not be suitable to carry out a small factory extension or to build a single house on an infill site in an urban location. The overhead costs of that size of organization would be such as to make it impossible for the company to carry out the work for an economic price.

At the other end of the scale, a one-man firm, used only to jobbing work and small alterations and extensions, would probably be out of its depth in handling a contract for the erection of even a modest-sized reinforced concrete office block. Such a firm, with little experience of estimating and probably none in the pricing of bills of quantities, would be likely to tender at too low a level by failing to include for all the costs involved. If given the contract, the firm would no doubt soon get into difficulties and probably would end up in disaster.

The client's professional advisers should aim to find a contracting company (a) that is financially stable and has a good business record, (b) for which the size of the project is neither too small nor too large (c) that has a reputation for good-quality workmanship and efficient organization and (*d*) that has a good record of industrial relations.

There are three principal methods of choosing a contractor: (*a*) open tendering, (*b*) selective tendering and (*c*) nomination.

Open tendering

This is initiated by the client's project manager, architect or quantity surveyor advertising in local newspapers and/or the technical press, inviting contractors to apply for tender documents and to tender in competition for carrying out the work, the main characteristics of which are given. Usually a deposit is required in order to discourage frivolous applications, the deposit being returnable on the submission of a *bona fide* tender.

Advantages

1 There can be no charge of favouritism as might be brought where a selected list is drawn up (this is of concern particularly to local authorities who, probably for this reason more than any other, tend to use open tendering more than other clients).

2 An opportunity is provided for a capable firm to submit a tender, which might not be included on a selected list.

3 It should secure maximum benefit from competition (it may not always do so, however, as may be seen from the disadvantages below).

Disadvantages

1 There is a danger that the lowest tender may be submitted by a firm inexperienced in preparing tenders (particularly if bills of quantities are used) and whose tender is only lowest as a consequence of having made the most or the largest errors.

2 There is no guarantee that the lowest tenderer is sufficiently capable or financially stable. Although obtaining references will provide some safeguard, there may be little time in which to do so.

3 Total cost of tendering is increased as all the tenderers will have to recoup their costs eventually through those tenders which are successful. The result can only be an increase in the general level of construction costs.

Open tendering was deprecated in the Banwell Report.[1] Consequently central government departments and most local authorities do not use this method of obtaining tenders. There tends, however, to be an increase in its use by local authorities in times of national economic difficulties with attendant public expenditure cuts, presumably because it is assumed that the more tenderers there are, the lower the price for which the work can be carried out.

Selective tendering

Selective tendering may be either *single stage* or *two stage*, depending on whether the full benefits of competition are desired (in which case single stage tendering is used) or whether limited competition plus earlier commencement of the works on site is considered advantageous (using two stage tendering). The NJCC has issued a *Code of Procedure* for each method.[2] It has also issued a Code for Design and Build contracts, using either the single stage or the two stage procedure,[3] and recommendations for tendering for industrialized building projects.[4] (Further references to 'the *Codes*' in this chapter relate to the first two.)

Single stage selective tendering

Under this procedure, a short list is drawn up of contractors who are considered to be suitable to carry out the proposed project. The names may be selected from an approved list or 'panel' maintained by the client (as many public authorities do), or may be specially chosen.

In the latter case the contractors may be invited, through suitably worded advertisements in the press, to apply to be considered for inclusion in the tender list. This gives the client the opportunity to exclude any firms thought to be unsuitable and to limit the number of tenderers. At the same time, it gives any firm the opportunity to apply to be considered.

It is recommended that the number of tenderers should be limited to between five and eight, depending on the size and nature of the contract. If the firms on the list are all ones which are reputable, well-established and suitable for the proposed work, and the client fixes the construction time, then the selection is resolved into a question of price alone and the contract can be safely awarded to the firm submitting the most favourable tender.

Advantages

1 It ensures that only capable and approved firms submit tenders.

2 It tends to reduce the aggregate cost of tendering.

Disadvantage

1 The cost level of the tenders received will be higher, owing to their being less competition and also to the higher calibre of the tenderers.

Nomination

This is sometimes referred to as *single tendering* and is, in effect, a special case of selective tendering, the short list containing only one name. It is used when the client has a preference for a particular firm, often because it has done satisfactory work for him before.

Obviously, if only one firm tenders for a job, competition is eliminated and that will, almost inevitably, lead to a higher price. The client may think it is worth paying more, however, in return for a quicker job or one of better quality than he might otherwise get. One should be fairly certain, however, that a worthwhile benefit will accrue before advising a client to nominate rather than go out to competitive tender.

When a contractor is nominated, the contract sum will be arrived at by a process of negotiation. This may be done using bills of quantities or schedules of rates, but instead of the contractor pricing the tender document on his own and submitting his tender to be accepted or rejected, the rates and prices are discussed and agreed until eventually a total price is arrived at which is acceptable to both sides.

Usually the negotiation will be conducted between one of the contractor's senior estimators and the PQS (either a partner, associate or senior assistant). To facilitate the procedure, one party will usually price the tender document first of all, to provide a basis for the negotiation. The other party will then go through the rates and prices, ticking off those which are acceptable and then the two surveyors will meet to negotiate the unticked ones. When agreement on the whole is reached, a contract will be entered into between the client and the contractor.

Serial tendering

Sometimes, when a large project is to be carried out in successive phases, a combination of selective tendering and nomination is employed. This is sometimes called *serial tendering*. The contractor is chosen for the first phase by means of selective competitive tendering. The accepted tender forms the basis of payment for the resulting contract in the normal way. The tender is also used for the second and later phases, provision being made for so doing in the initial contract by the inclusion of a formula for updating the prices. Alternatively, the contract for the first phase may specify negotiation of new rates, based upon the tendered prices, as the means of determining the payment for each successive phase in the series.

The purpose of serial tendering is to gain the benefits of continuity. The contractor for the first phase of the project will have his site organization set up, his offices, mess and storage huts, etc., already in use and plant of various kinds on the site. When the second phase commences, these facilities will be already available, thus allowing a smooth transition with much less additional expense than if a different contractor were to be employed.

In addition, the contractor's workforce will be familiar with the details of the construction after building the first phase and thus should be able to work more speedily and efficiently on the second and subsequent stages.

Two stage selective tendering

This procedure is used when it is desired to obtain the benefits of competition and at the same time to have the advantage of bringing a contractor into the planning of the project, thus making use of his practical knowledge and expertise. It may also result in an earlier start on site.

The first stage aims to select a suitable contractor by means of limited competition. The second stage is a process of negotiation with the selected contractor on the basis of the first stage tender.

First, a short list of tenderers is prepared, as described for single stage tendering. The *Code* recommends a maximum of six names on the list (four in the case of specialist engineering contracts) and also suggests matters for consideration when drawing up the list.

First stage

When being invited to tender, tenderers are informed of the second stage intentions, including any special requirements of the client and the nature and extent of the contractor's participation during the second stage. Tenderers are asked to tender on the basis of any or all of the following:

(i) an *ad hoc* schedule of rates, consisting of the main or significant items only;

(ii) a detailed build-up of prices for the main Preliminaries items;

(iii) a construction programme showing estimated times and labour and plant resources which would be used, and also construction methods;

(iv) details of all-in labour rates and main materials prices and discounts which would go into the build-up of the detailed tender;

(v) percentage additions for profit and overheads;

(vi) proposed sub-letting of work, with additions for profit and attendance.

During this stage, discussion with each of the tenderers may be conducted in order to elucidate their proposals and to enable the contractors to make any suggestions with regard to design and/or construction methods. When these procedures have been concluded, a contractor is selected to go forward to the second stage. It is important that, in accepting the first stage tender, the parties define procedures for either of them to withdraw, should the second stage negotiations prove abortive, and what, if any, payment may be due to either party in that event, including reimbursement of the contractor for any site works he may have carried out.

Second stage

During this stage, finalization of the design proceeds in consultation with the selected contractor, and bills of quantities (or other detailed document describing the proposed works) are prepared and priced on the basis of the first stage tender. Negotiation on the prices will follow until agreement is reached and a total contract sum arrived at, when the parties will enter into a contract for the construction works.

When time is pressing and it is desired to start work on site before final agreement is reached, a contract may be signed earlier. In that case, when the PQS considers that a sufficient measure of agreement has been reached on the prices for the principal parts of the work, he will recommend the client to proceed with arrangements for the signing of a contract. This is not recommended in the *Code*, but the client may consider that it is worth taking a risk in order to speed up the project.

TENDER DOCUMENTS

The number and nature of the tender documents will vary with the type of contract. They will include some or all of the following.

Conditions of the contract

This document sets out the obligations and rights of the parties and the detailed conditions under which a subsequent contract will operate. If a standard form, such as the JCT Form, is used it will not be sent out with the invitation to tender, it being assumed that the tenderers will have a copy or can readily obtain one. The clause headings will, however, be listed in the first (Preliminaries) section of the bills of quantities and/or specification.

Bills of quantities

These are normally used for lump sum contracts of more than say, £50,000. Tenderers should be sent two copies of the bills,[5] one for return to the architect or PQS with the tender, the other for the contractor to keep as a copy of his submitted prices. If the tenderers are not required to submit priced bills with their tenders, only one copy need be sent to them initially. A second copy will then be sent at the time of requesting submission of the priced bills.

Specification

In the case of lump sum contracts without bills of quantities, a detailed specification will be supplied to tenderers. Sometimes a specification will be supplied in addition to bills of quantities where they are used, but this is exceptional nowadays. A specification may be in a form for detailed pricing.

Schedule of works

As an alternative to a specification in the case of 'without quantities' contracts, tenderers may be supplied with a Schedule of Works. This lists the work comprised in the contract under appropriate headings. The tenderers may be required to price the schedule.

Drawings

Normally general arrangement drawings will be provided, showing site location, position of the building(s) on and means of access to the site and floor plans and elevations. Tenderers are not normally given working drawings as they are not considered to be necessary for pricing purposes, full descriptions of the work being incorporated in the bills or specification. Tenderers are informed, however, that they can inspect drawings not supplied to them, at the architect's office.

Form of tender

This is a pre-printed formal statement, often in the form of a letter, in which a tenderer fills in, in the blank spaces, his name and address and the sum of money for which he offers to carry out the work shown on the drawings and described in the bills of quantities or specification. An example of a typical Form of Tender is given in Appendix C to the *Code of Procedure for Single Stage Selective Tendering*.[6]

Return envelope

Each tenderer should be supplied with a pre-addressed envelope clearly marked 'Tender for (name of project)'. This will ensure that tenders are recognized as such when received and will not be prematurely opened.

Tenderers should be asked to acknowledge in writing receipt of the tender documents.

TENDERING PROCEDURE

Preliminary enquiry

It is recommended practice (although not always followed) to send, about a month beforehand, to each of the firms from whom it is proposed to invite a tender, a preliminary enquiry[7] to ascertain that they are willing to submit a *bona fide* tender. This avoids the situation of contractors declining to tender or, if they prefer not to decline although not wanting to tender, submitting a 'cover price', i.e. a price which is high enough to be well above the lowest tender.

Sufficient information about the project should be given in the preliminary enquiry letter to enable each contractor to decide whether he is in a position to comply and, if so, whether he would be able in view of other commitments, to carry out the contract if it is awarded to him.

If for any reason, a firm which has signified its willingness to tender, is not included in the final short list of tenderers, it should be informed of the fact immediately, as other tender invitations may be under consideration.

Period for preparation of tenders

It is important that tenderers are given sufficient time to make all necessary enquiries from suppliers, sub-traders, etc. and the date for return of tenders should be fixed so as to allow for the amount of work likely to be involved in preparing a tender for a job of the size and character of the proposed project. Four weeks is recommended as a minimum period, although it is possible, in exceptional cases, for less time to be adequate.

A time of day (often noon) should be specified as the latest time for tenders to be received on the date fixed. Any tenders arriving later should be returned and should be excluded from the competition.

Parity of tendering

It is of paramount importance that all tenders should be based on the same information. Consequently, all the tender documents must be identical. It would be possible, for example, for some copies of a drawing to contain the latest amendments while other copies are of the unamended drawing.

Not infrequently, a tenderer will telephone the architect or PQS about an item in the bills of quantities or a clause in the specification. He may question the accuracy of a quantity or have been told by a supplier that a specified material is no longer marketed. Such queries must, of course, be answered and must be dealt with promptly. But, whatever the reply given to the enquirer, if it adds to or varies in any way the information given in the tender documents, it must be communicated to all tenderers. This should be done immediately by telephone and then confirmed in writing. The same procedure must be followed if an error is discovered by the PQS in the bills or specification or other tender document or if it is decided to extend the time for the receipt of tenders. Tenderers should be asked to confirm in writing the receipt of every written communication of additional or varied information immediately.

Equally in pursuance of the principle of parity of tendering, bills of quantities should be priced as drawn up by the PQS and likewise where tenders are based on specifications or schedules of rates. A tenderer sometimes wants to price for an alternative material which he considers to be just as good as that specified but which he can obtain more cheaply. Or he may want to allow for an alternative form, method or order of construction. The procedure which he should adopt in such a case is to price the tender documents as printed and to submit, in an accompanying letter or other suitable form, details of the alternative material or form of construction etc. with the consequential effect on his tender sum.

If a tender is qualified in any respect which it is considered has given the tenderer an unfair advantage over the others, or which makes the comparison of the tenders unreasonable, then that tenderer should be given the opportunity of withdrawing the qualification without amending the tender sum.[8] If he is unwilling to do so, his tender should be rejected.

It is desirable that the number of variables in tenders should be reduced as far as possible so that they are made more readily comparable. One of these variables is the length of the construction period and it is common practice for this to be specified by the client. If a contractor wants to offer to do the work in a shorter time, then the procedure which he should follow is the same as for any other qualification to the printed documents, as described above. If the contractor objects to the period as unreasonably short, however, he should raise the matter with the architect during the tender period. If it is decided to extend the construction period, then all tenderers must be informed, as this may well affect their tender sums.

Opening tenders

Tenders are normally returnable to the architect or project manager (sometimes to the PQS). A formal procedure should be followed for opening them to eliminate any suspicion of irregularities. No tender must be opened before the latest time for submission and the specially-marked envelopes supplied with the tender documents are intended to eliminate accidental opening. There can be no possibility then of anyone communicating to another tenderer the amount of a competitor's tender.

As little time as reasonably possible should be allowed to elapse before opening tenders and they should all be opened at the same time, preferably in the presence of the architect and PQS and, if he so wishes, the client. In the case of public bodies, tenders are usually opened by, or in the presence of, the chairman of the committee responsible for the project.

Notifying tenderers

A tender list should be drawn up and sent to all tenderers as soon as possible after the meeting at which the tenders were opened. This is so that each contractor may know whether his tender was successful or not and so be better able to judge his future commitments and know how to respond to any other invitation to tender. The list should contain all the tenderers' names arranged in alphabetical order and all the tender sums in ascending order. It should not disclose which tenderer submitted which amount but, of course, each will be able to identify the position of his own tender in relation to the lowest. At the same time, all but the three lowest should be informed that their tenders have not been successful. The preparation of the tender list and its communication to tenderers is a duty which often falls to the PQS to carry out.

REFERENCES

1. *The Placing and Management of Contracts for Building and Civil Engineering Work* (London: HMSO, 1964).
2. NJCC, *Code of Procedure for Single Stage Selective Tendering* (London: RIBA Publications Ltd, 1977). NJCC, *Code of Procedure for Two Stage Selective Tendering* (London: RIBA Publications Ltd, 1983).
3. NJCC, *Code of Procedure for Selective Tendering for Design and Build* (London: RIBA Publications Ltd, 1985).
4. NJCC, *Tendering Procedure for Industrialized Building Projects* (London: RIBA Publications Ltd, 1974).
5. NJCC, *Code of Procedure for Single Stage Selective Tendering* (London: RIBA Publications Ltd, 1977), Appendix B.
6. ibid., Appendix C.
7. ibid., Appendix A.
8. ibid., para. 4.4.3.

5

Examining and reporting on tenders

EXAMINATION OF LOWEST TENDER

Once the lowest tender has been identified, the PQS will proceed to look at it in detail. There will usually be supporting documents such as schedules of rates and, in many cases, bills of quantities requiring careful scrutiny. If there are bills, the lowest tenderer will be asked to submit his priced bills for examination (if not sent with his tender), at the same time being informed that his was the lowest tender and it is therefore under consideration.

To save time in the event of the lowest tender proving unsatisfactory, the next lowest, or the next two lowest tenderers, may also be asked to submit their priced bills. They should be informed that although their tenders were not the lowest, they are under consideration. Opinions vary amongst PQSs as to whether the second or third lowest tenderer's bills should be looked at until the lowest has been rejected. Some say they should not, as being of no concern at all should the lowest tender be accepted. Others take the view that there may be errors in the second or third bills which, if corrected, would make one of them the lowest. From the basic legal point of view that it is the originally tendered total sums which are all-important, it seems logical that, even if the three (or two) lowest tenderers' bills are called for, the second and third ones should not be looked at until the lowest tender has been rejected. Should the lowest be satisfactory, the other bills should be returned to the contractors unexamined.

The PQS, when examining bills of quantities, schedules of rates, etc., will look for errors of any kind and for any anomalies or pecularities which, in his opinion, make it unwise for the client to enter into a contractual relationship with the tenderer. It should be remembered, however, that whilst it is made clear to tenderers when tendering that the client does not bind himself to accept the lowest or any tender, contractors naturally expect that there will be sound reasons for rejecting the lowest tender. The PQS must therefore be able to provide those reasons in the event of the lowest tender not being accepted.

It has already been stated that the important factor in a lump sum tender is the total sum for which the contractor offers to carry out the work. If that offer is accepted, then, legally, a binding contract exists. It may be asked therefore 'Why examine the tender in detail?' It is because of the uses made of the component parts of a tender subsequently that any errors in the bills of quantities/schedules of rates need to be identified and satisfactorily dealt with. Otherwise, problems will almost certainly arise during the course of the contract and in the settlement of the final account. For example, an error may have occurred in a bill when multiplying the quantity of an item by the unit rate and thus an incorrect amount for that item is shown. If the error were not corrected and subsequently the item was affected by a variation order, say, halving the quantity, what is to be done? Should half the total amount be omitted or should the PQS omit half the quantity at the unit rate shown? The latter course could result in the omission of an amount which is greater than the incorrect total for the item. It is to avoid such difficulties that errors should be found and dealt with in a satisfactory manner.

A further reason is that the examination of the tender details is likely to reveal whether an arithmetical error of such a magnitude has occurred that it would not be wise to hold the contractor to the tender sum because he would then be working at a much reduced profit (assuming the tender sum to be too low). If such an error were in the contractor's favour, then it would be unfair to the client to have to pay more than the job was worth.

The things which the PQS will look for when examining bills or schedules of rates will be of the following kinds.

Arithmetical errors

These may occur in the item extensions (i.e. the multiplication of the quantities by the unit rates), in the totalling of a page, in the transfer of page totals to collections or summaries, in the calculation of percentage additions on the General Summary or by rounding-off the bill total when carrying it to the Form of Tender.

Pricing errors

These are patent errors *not* matters of opinion as to whether a rate is high or low. A patent error will sometimes occur where, in the transition from cube to superficial measurement, or from superficial measurement to linear, the estimator has continued to use the basic cube rate for the superficial items, or the basic superficial rate for the linear items. Such errors are obvious and not the subject of opinion. Another type of patent error is where, apparently by an oversight, an item has not been priced at all which one would normally expect to be priced.

Again identical items in different sections of the bills may have been priced differently without there being any good reason. These differences usually arise because the estimator has not remembered that an identical item has occurred before or, if he has, has not bothered to look back to see what rate had been used. This type of error is not uncommon in housing contracts, where there are separate bills for each house type, and in elemental bills where items recur in different elements.

Pricing method

Sometimes a tenderer will not price most, or any, of the 'Preliminaries' items, their value being included in some or all of the measured rates. This might create difficulty should any adjustment of the value of 'Preliminaries' become necessary.

Some contractors may price all the measured items at nett rates (i.e. exclusive of any profit and overheads), showing the latter as an inserted lump sum on the General Summary page of the bills. This is unsatisfactory when using the bill rates later on and the tenderer should be asked to distribute the lump sum throughout the bills or to agree to its being treated as a single percentage addition to all the prices.

Again, a contractor may price the excavation, concrete work and brickwork sections of the job (i.e. those sections which will largely be completed in the early months of the job) at inflated prices, balancing these with low rates in the finishings sections. His object would be to secure higher payments in the early valuations, thus improving his cash flow position. This procedure would tend to work against the client's interest, particularly if the contractor were to go into liquidation before the contract was completed. Such a pricing policy might possibly indicate a less stable financial situation than previously thought.

The contractor is entitled, of course, to build up his tender as he thinks fit and cannot be required to change any of his rates or prices. However, contractors usually recognize and accept the need to correct obvious errors and the PQS would be imprudent on his part not to do so. As regards pricing strategy, this is usually considered to be a matter for the contractor's decision, the remedy being, if the PQS has genuine grounds for concern about it, for him to recommend the client not to accept the tender.

Basic prices list

The contract provisions may require the contractor to submit a list of the basic prices of materials upon which his tender is based. This will be used in order to adjust the contract sum for any fluctuations in the costs of materials during the contract period (see pp. 135 and 230). The list should be scrutinized to ensure that the prices quoted are the current market prices of the materials named, including delivery to the site in full loads. If the PQS considers it necessary, he should ask the contractor to submit recent quotations for each of the listed materials.

Further points to note in regard to tenders which are not based on bills of firm quantities are as follows.

Tenders based on bills of approximate quantities

The rates for items of which the quantities are likely to be substantially increased upon measurement of the work as executed should be carefully scrutinized, as these may affect the total cost of the job considerably.

Tenders based on drawings and specification only

The schedule of the principal rates which have been used in the preparation of the tender should be looked at closely as these rates will be used in the pricing of any variations which may be subsequently ordered. If there is likely to be much dayworks, the percentage additions to prime costs which the tenderer has quoted may also become significant.

Tenders based on ad hoc schedule of rates

The rates for items which are likely to be significant in terms of quantity need careful scrutiny. The above comment in regard to dayworks will also apply here.

REPORTING ON TENDERS

The PQS must report to the project manager or the architect and the client as soon as his examination of the tenders is complete. He must remember that the purpose of the report is to enable the client to decide whether to accept any of the tenders and, if so, which one. Consequently, it should concentrate on matters of importance and minor matters, such as the details of arithmetical errors, should be excluded.

The form of the report will vary according to the nature of the tender documents but usually will include the following:

(a) the opinion of the PQS as to the price level i.e. that the tender is high, low or about the level expected;

(b) the quality of the pricing, indicating any detectable pricing method or policy;

(c) the extent of errors and inconsistencies in pricing and the action taken in regard to them;

(d) the details of any qualifications to the tender;

(e) the likely total cost of the project, if not a lump sum contract;

(f) a recommendation as to acceptance or otherwise.

The examination and reporting on tenders for *design and build contracts* (see p. 28) is not as straightforward a matter as for other types of contract. There will be a number of variables, making comparison between tenders difficult. Apart from price differences, they will vary in the construction time, constructional form, quality of finishes, degree of maintenance likely to be required subsequently, and perhaps the anticipated cost of running and maintaining specialist installations. In his report, the PQS will need to consider all the tenders since there will not be a lowest tender as such. He will need to set out in a clear and easily-assimilated form the relative savings, benefits, merits and demerits between the packages offered. He should, nevertheless, make his recommendation as to which one, if any, the client should accept.

Figure 8 is a report on the tenders for the contract described in Appendix A and illustrates the application of some of the foregoing principles.

DEALING WITH ERRORS, ETC.

In the case of tenders not based on bills of quantities, the scope for detection of errors, etc. is limited and correction of any which are discovered is usually a straightforward matter of adjusting any erroneous rates, with the contractor's agreement.

If a lump sum tender based on drawings and specification only shows a breakdown of the total and this contains arithmetical errors, then correction should be done in a similar way to that described for bills of quantities, so far as is applicable.

Two alternative ways of dealing with errors in bills are recommended in Section 6 of the *Code of Procedure for Single Stage Selective Tendering*.[1] The first is the traditional procedure of informing the tenderer of the errors and asking him whether he wishes to confirm his tender, notwithstanding the errors (which may be favourable or unfavourable to him), or whether he wishes to withdraw it. This procedure accords with the basic principle of the law of contract whereby an offer is made to provide goods and/ or services for a certain consideration and the offerer may withdraw his offer at any time before its acceptance.

The second course of action is to inform the tenderer of the errors and to ask him whether he wishes to confirm his tender, notwithstanding the errors, or whether he wishes to correct genuine errors. If he chooses to correct his errors and the revised tender sum is then higher than the next on the list, then his tender will be set aside and the one now lowest will be proceeded with in a similar way instead. A recommendation similar to this second alternative is contained in Section 7 of the *Code of Procedure for Two Stage Selective Tendering*[2] in relation to first stage tenders.

It should be noted that the term 'genuine errors' means inadvertent arithmetical errors and patent pricing errors, as defined earlier. It does not include errors which the estimator may have made in the build-up of a bill rate or price. The provision for the correction of genuine errors does not give the contractor the

Shops and Flats, Thames Street, Skinton, Middlesex

REPORT ON TENDERS

1.   Tender list. Six tenders were received as follows:

Contractor	Tender sum
Beecon Ltd	£ 495,000
W.E. Bildit Ltd	£ 514,800
E.A.Myson Ltd	£ 520,000
Thorn (Contractors) Ltd	£ 526,500
Smith & Sons Ltd	£ 538,200
Brown & Green Ltd	£ 576,000

The lowest tender is 3.85% below the second lowest tender.

It is also within the amount of our last amended cost plan dated 20 November 1986 , which was in the sum of £504,000.

2.   Bills of quantities. The priced bills of quantities submitted by the lowest tenderer, Beecon Ltd, have been examined and the following is a report on our findings.

3.   Pricing

3.1   The general level of the pricing is, in our opinion, slightly lower than average for this class of work, even allowing for the present economic climate. We do not consider, however, that this should be a cause for concern in this instance as Beecon Ltd are well-established contractors in the area with a reputation for good quality work. Also it is known that they particularly wanted to obtain this contract because of its prominent location and its proximity to their head office.

3.2   The pricing is consistent throughout, with no serious anomalies or detectable adverse characteristics.

3.3   A number of arithmetical errors were discovered and have been corrected in accordance with the provisions set out in the tender documents. Beecon Ltd have elected to stand by their tender sum of £495,000 notwithstanding the errors. Had the tender sum been amended, it would have been reduced by £9,112, which is the nett amount of the errors.

4.   Recommendation. We recommend that the contract be awarded to Beecon Ltd in consideration of the sum of £495,000.

Kewess & Partners
52 High Street
Urbiston
Surrey

6 February 1987

Figure 8

opportunity of increasing any rates or prices which on reflection he realizes are too low nor of pricing any items which were intentionally left unpriced.

One reason why the second alternative has been introduced is that, because of the large sums involved in most construction projects, it is in clients' interests to allow the correction of such errors as have the effect of increasing the tender sum, if to do so leaves the tender still in the lowest position. The contractor will be happier and the client will be paying a lower price than if the contractor felt he had no alternative but to withdraw. In any case, it is not in the client's interest to have a discontented contractor from the start of the contract, who feels that he is beginning the contract with an expectation of a reduced profit.

The *Code* recommends that it is decided from the outset which of the alternative methods of dealing with any errors will be used and that this information is included in the preliminary enquiry to tenderers, the formal invitation to tender and the Form of Tender.

When the contractor elects to confirm his tender, his errors must still be dealt with so that the priced document is arithmetically correct and consistent throughout. This is so that when the rates and prices are used subsequently, difficulties which would otherwise arise will be eliminated (see p. 55 under the heading *'Examination of lowest tender'*). The correction of errors must, of course, be done in consultation and agreement with the contractor. The PQS will normally draw up a list of errors, etc., which he will agree with the contractor and the PQS will then amend the priced document accordingly.

The procedure for the correction of errors in bills is as follows:

(*a*) If the original text has been altered without authorization, the alteration(s) should be deleted and prices adjusted accordingly.

(*b*) All errors of the kinds described earlier (i.e. arithmetical and patent pricing errors) should be corrected and the corrections carried through from page totals to collections, from collections to summaries and from summaries to general summary. The incorrect amounts should be ruled through with a single line and the correct ones written above, neatly and clearly.

(*c*) A sum, equal to the nett amount of the aggregated errors, should be inserted on the General Summary immediately before the final total as an addition or deduction, as appropriate. This will have the effect of adjusting the corrected bill total to the amount stated on the Form of Tender (which, it should be noted, in some instances may not be the same sum as the original total of the bills).

This nett addition or deduction equal to the errors is, in effect, the aggregate of adjustments to every rate and price in the bills, excluding any contingency sum, provisional and prime cost sums and Preliminaries (if deducted). Accordingly, any subsequent use of a rate or price from the bills or of one based upon rates or prices in the bills, must be subjected to an equivalent adjustment. To facilitate this, the balancing sum (i.e. the nett amount of the errors) is calculated as a percentage of the value of the builder's work. The contract copies of the priced bills should be endorsed with a statement that all the rates and prices (other than contingency, provisional and prime cost sums) are to be considered as increased or reduced (as appropriate) by that percentage. The example in Figure 9 illustrates how the process may be effected.

All PQSs do not agree on what constitutes 'builder's work' for the purpose of calculating the adjusting percentage referred to in the last paragraph. The *Codes* say that in addition to the fixed sums mentioned above, the value of Preliminaries items should also be excluded. Turner[3] does not agree, taking the view that the latter are just as much the contractor's own prices as those applied to measured items. This seems a reasonable view, particularly as arithmetical errors may occur just as easily in the Preliminaries as in the measured sections of the bills.

In the calculation on page 63 the Preliminaries have been deducted from the contract sum in accordance with the *Codes*. The bills were those submitted in support of the tender for the contract described in Appendix A, in which the corrected amounts are shown in the Summary of Bill No 3 and in the General Summary.

REFERENCES

1. NJCC, *Code of Procedure for Single Stage Selective Tendering* (London: RIBA Publications Ltd, 1977).
2. NJCC, *Code of Procedure for Two Stage Selective Tendering* (London: RIBA Publications Ltd, 1982).
3. TURNER, DENNIS F., *Quantity Surveying Practice and Administration* (London: George Godwin Ltd, 3rd Ed., 1983), p. 125.

List of errors in priced bills submitted by Beecon Ltd

Page no	Item ref.	Type of error	Effect of error on total of tender:	
			Increased by £	Decreased by £
25	–	Page total	100.00	
30	–	Page total		6.00
48	C	Item extension	65.20	
75	–	Page total transferred incorrectly		0.45
86	L	Item extension		18.50
103	D	Item extension	460.00	
140	–	Page total		500.00
General Summary	–	Page total transferred incorrectly from p. 108		27.00
General Summary	–	Subtotal	10 000.00	
		Total rounded down on Form of Tender		961.25
			10 625.20	1513.20
			1513.20	
		Nett amount of errors	9112.00	

The following pages show how the error in item D on p. 103 of the bills was dealt with and the consequential correction of totals, also the corrections to the Summary and General Summary, of all the errors listed above. On the General Summary is shown the sum added to balance the nett error and also the endorsement. The adjusting percentage referred to in the endorsement has been calculated thus:

$$\frac{9112.00}{485\,888.00 - (35\,660.00 + 117\,724.00 + 5820.36)} \times 100 = 2.79\%$$

This calculation should be shown on the General Summary page in a convenient position or on the facing page.

Figure 9 Example of correction of errors in bills of quantities

GLAZING

GLASS IN OPENINGS £ p

OQ quality sheet glass

A 4 mm Glass and glazing to wood)
with bradded wood beads in panes)
over 1 m²) 71 m² 20.60 1462·60

B 4 mm Ditto but in panes over 0.50 m²)
and not exceeding 1 m²) 60 m² 21.51 1290·60

C 4 mm Ditto but in panes over 0.10 m²)
and not exceeding 0.50 m²) 16 m² 23.21 371·36

D 4 mm Ditto and glazing to metal with)
mastic and spring glazing clips in)
panes over 0.50 m² and not) 1020·74
exceeding 1 m²) 46 m² 22.19 ~~1480·74~~

Rolled glass, pattern group 2

E 3 mm Glass and glazing to wood)
with bradded wood beads in panes)
over 0.10 m² and not exceeding)
0.50 m²) 20 m² 18.34 366·80

Rolled Georgian wired rough cast glass

F 6 mm Glass and glazing to wood)
with bradded wood beads in panes)
up to 1260 mm wide and up to)
3700 mm long) 48 m² 33.80 1622·40

Rolled Georgian wired polished plate glass

G 6 mm Glass and glazing to wood)
with bradded wood beads in panes)
over 0.10 m² and not exceeding)
0.50 m²) 17 m² 49.85 7·45

GG quality clear plate float glass

H 6 mm Glass in sliding hatch doors,)
size 475 mm wide × 570 mm high,)
ground on all edges and with one)
ground and shaped finger grip) 36 No. 22.86 822·96
sinking

7804·91
Carried to Collection £ ~~8264·91~~

103

Figure 9 *(cont.)*

GLAZING (*cont.*)

SUNDRIES		£	p
A Glazing strips as described and bedding to edges of 3 mm glass)	) 188 m	0.65	122.20
B Ditto and bedding to edges of 4 mm) glass	178 m	0.65	115.70
C Ditto and bedding to edges of 6 mm) glass	538 m	0.65	349.70
PROTECTION			
D Allow for protecting the work in this) Section)	Item	— — —	

Carried to Collection £ 587.60

COLLECTION	£	p
		7 804.91
Page 103	— —	8 264 91
Page 104		587.60
		8 392.51
GLAZING Total Carried to Summary		£8 052 51

Figure 9 (*cont.*)

BILL NO 3 – SHOPS AND FLATS

SUMMARY

PAGE		£ p
26	Excavation and earthwork	31 174.54 ~~31 274.54~~
33	Concrete work	54 466.13 ~~54 460.13~~
44	Brickwork and blockwork	45 515.80
69	Woodwork	55 287.79 ~~55 352.99~~
75	Metalwork	9387.72 ~~9387.27~~
89	Plumbing and mechanical engineering installations	27 349.36 ~~27 330.86~~
92	Electrical installations	8404.92
102	Floor, wall and ceiling finishings	23 100.51
104	Glazing	8392.51 ~~8852.51~~
107	Painting and decorating	17 516.85
	TOTAL CARRIED TO GENERAL SUMMARY	280 596.13 £~~281 196.38~~

108

Figure 9 (*cont.*)

GENERAL SUMMARY

PAGE		£ p
15	Bill No 1 – Preliminaries	35 660.00
19	Bill No 2 – Site clearance	5 531.00
108	Bill No 3 – Shops and flats	2 80 596.13 ~~281 169.30~~
143	Bill No 4 – External works	40 556.51 ~~40 056.51~~
147	Bill No 5 – Prime cost sums and dayworks	117 724.00
		480 067·64 ~~490 140.89~~

Add for:
Insurance against injury to persons
and property as item 5C   3632.00

All Risks Insurance as item 5C   811.36

Water for the Works as item 13A   1377.00
                                                  _____
                                                  485 888 .00

Add to adjust for errors   911 2.00
                                                  _____
                                                  495 000.00
TOTAL CARRIED TO FORM OF TENDER   ~~495 961.25*~~

All rates and prices herein (excluding
preliminaries, prime cost and provisional
sums) are to be considered as increased by
2.79%.

Signed .... 148 Signed ....

Figure 9 (*cont.*)

*Carried to Form of Tender as £495 000

6

The contract

Under the general law of contract, when a party makes an offer to provide goods and/or services for some certain consideration and the party to whom the offer is made accepts it, then, provided it does not involve any illegal act, a contract which is enforceable at law exists. This is no less the case in the construction world than in any other sphere of business or industry. The offer is made by a contractor who tenders to carry out specified construction works in return for a money payment and upon the acceptance of that offer by the client promoting the project, a binding contract comes into being.

It is desirable that the client's acceptance should be in writing and that it should be given as soon as possible after receipt of tenders. If there is any appreciable delay of, say, one to two months or more, then it will be necessary to obtain the contractor's confirmation that his price still stands or what the increase in his price is, due to rising costs.

THE CONTRACT DOCUMENTS

The number and nature of the contract documents will normally correspond with those of the tender documents (see p. 48). They may be some or all of the following.

Form of contract

This is the principal document and will often be a printed standard form, such as one of the variants of the JCT Form. This consists of three parts: (i) the Articles of Agreement, which is the actual contract which the parties sign; (ii) The Conditions of the contract (sub-divided into four parts), which set out the obligations and rights of the parties and detail the conditions under which the contract is to be carried out; and (iii) Supplemental Provisions (the VAT Agreement), which sets out the rights and liabilities of the parties in regard to value added tax.

Bills of quantities

Any errors in the bills must be corrected in the manner described in Chapter 5 and any necessary adjustments to rates and prices must be clearly and neatly made.

Specification

Under the 'with quantities' variants of the JCT Form, the specification (if one exists) is not a contract document but it is under the 'without quantities' variants. In the latter case, the specification may have been prepared in a form for detailed pricing and have been priced by the contractor when tendering. If this is not the case, the contractor may have been asked to submit with his tender a Contract Sum Analysis. This shows a breakdown of the tender sum in sufficient detail to enable variations and provisional sum work to be valued, the price adjustment formulae to be applied and the preparation of interim certificates to be facilitated.

JCT Practice Note 23[1] gives a guide to the identification of specified parts of the contract sum and the breakdown of the remainder into parcels of work. A Contract Sum Analysis may not be required where a Schedule of Rates is used. In cases where a Contract Sum Analysis or a Schedule of Rates is provided, it is signed by the parties and attached to the contract, but is not a contract document. However, the specification is a contract document in such cases.

Schedule of Works

Where bills of quantities do not form part of the contract (for example, under the JCT Standard Form without quantities), the contractor may be sent a Schedule of Works for pricing when tendering, instead of a specification. If so, the priced Schedule of Works will become a contract document.

Schedule of rates

Where bills of quantities are not provided, a schedule of rates is usually necessary as a basis for pricing the work in measured contracts and for pricing variations in the case of lump sum contracts. Such schedules are described on pp. 14–15.

Drawings

The contract drawings are not limited to those (if any) sent to the contractor with the invitation to tender but are all those which have been used in the preparation of the bills of quantities or specification.

It is important that the contract drawings are precisely defined, as amendments may be made to them during the period between inviting tenders and commencing the work on site. Such amendments may affect the value of the contract and, if they do, should be made the subject of Architect's Instructions. It is good practice therefore, for the PQS to certify in writing, on each of the drawings used for taking-off or specification purposes, that they were the ones so used.

PREPARATIONS FOR EXECUTING THE CONTRACT

The PQS is often regarded by architects as the expert in matters relating to the interpretation and application of the contract Conditions. Accordingly, it is not uncommon for the preparations for the signing of the contract to be the task of the PQS.

Each of the contract documents is important from a legal point of view. Both parties (and their agents) are bound by what is said in them. When a contract proceeds satisfactorily to completion and settlement, many of the details in those documents may not be referred to. They become all-important, however, when a contract runs into difficulties and particular statements in the documents may then come under close scrutiny. If there are ambiguities, discrepancies or contradictions in them, it may lead to delays, arbitration proceedings or even actions in the Courts, all of which are expensive as well as frustrating.

If such faults in the contract documents are due to the carelessness of the persons responsible for their preparation, their principals (i.e. the partners in the firm of PQSs or architects, as the case may be) may be liable for a claim for damages for negligence, which might prove very costly. Great care must be exercised therefore, in carrying out the task of preparing the documents for the execution of the contract.

Each of the contract documents as already listed will require attention, if only to facilitate the actual signing, and they will now be considered in turn.

Form of contract

The Articles of Agreement

The blank spaces must be filled in with the date and names and addresses of the employer and the contractor, a brief statement of the nature and location of the Works, the architect's name, the numbers of the contract drawings, the contract sum (in words and in figures) and the names and addresses respectively of the architect/contract administrator and quantity surveyor.

Where bills of quantities are not used and if, in consequence, a quantity surveyor is not appointed, an alternative Article is provided for the name to be given of the person exercising the quantity surveying functions. The Article not required should be struck out in a neat and clear manner.

In the 'local authorities' variants of the JCT Form, an alternative Article (3B) is given for use where the architectural functions are to be exercised by a contract administrator, being a person who is not a registered architect and again, the Article not required must be struck out.

There follow in the 'private' editions of the JCT Form, spaces for the signatures of the parties. The employer (or his representative) signs in the first space and the contractor (or his representative) signs in the second space. Each signature is followed by the signature of a witness. If both signatures are obtained at the same time, as is usual, the witness may be the same person in each instance.

When either party must, or wishes to, execute the contract under seal, as in the case of some local authorities and other public bodies and corporations, the spaces for signatures, referred to above, are left blank and the seals are affixed in the appropriate spaces indicated.

The 'local authorities' editions of the JCT Form have a blank page for the insertion of a suitable Attestation Clause in place of the printed clauses in the 'private' editions.

The Conditions

Some clauses of the Conditions in the JCT Form contain alternative wording. Attention is drawn to these alternatives in footnotes and to the need for appropriate deletions. Such deletions should be clearly and neatly made.

There may be need or desire for other alterations or additions to be made to the clauses of a standard form in a particular case. All such alterations and additions, as well as the alternatives to be deleted, should be specifically listed in the 'Preliminaries' section of the bills or specification and, if this has been done, the list may then be used as a check-list in the preparation of the standard form for executing the contract.

The blank spaces in the Appendix to the Conditions (see Appendix B, p. 235) should also be filled in, in accordance with a further list in the bills or specification. It should be noted that if nothing is stated against certain of the clause numbers, then specified time periods will apply.

The parties should initial each amendment to the printed document in the adjacent margin. This serves to confirm that all amendments were made before the contract was executed and that no amendment was made subsequent to that event.

Bills of quantities

The priced bills submitted by the contractor should show clearly all the amended and corrected rates and prices, etc., which have been agreed between the contractor and the PQS. If an adjusting amount, equal to the amount of the errors, has been entered in the General Summary, then an endorsement should be added indicating the percentage effect on the measured rates and prices (see p. 67). On the reverse of the last page a further endorsement should be added, saying 'These are the Contract Bills referred to in the Contract' with spaces for the signatures of the parties, set out in the same way as in the Articles of Agreement.

Specification

Where the specification is a contract document, all that is necessary is to endorse on the reverse of the last page the words 'This is the Specification referred to in the Contract' with spaces for the signatures as in the case of bills. The schedule of rates should show clearly all corrections and amendments which have been agreed between the PQS and the contractor. If, alternatively, a Contract Sum Analysis has been submitted, this should be signed by the parties and attached to the Specification or to the Contract Conditions.

Schedule of Works

If a priced Schedule of works has been submitted by the contractor when tendering, that will be a contract document instead of the specification. It should be endorsed in a similar manner as that described for specifications and be signed by the parties.

Drawings

It is desirable that each of the drawings should be endorsed either 'This is a contract drawing' or 'This drawing was used in the preparation of the bills of quantities' or some similar statement. Many firms have rubber stamps for this purpose.

Subsequent to the execution of the contract, the contract documents are kept either by the architect or by the PQS. The Employer and the Contractor have the right to inspect them at any reasonable time. (The 'local authorities' variant provides for these documents to remain in the custody of the Employer.)

COPIES OF CONTRACT DOCUMENTS

Immediately after the execution of the contract, the contractor should be given a certified copy of the Articles of Agreement, the Conditions of the Contract, the contract drawings, and the contract bills. In practice, the two copies of these documents are prepared at the same time so that they are identical, including all the initialling and the signatures. Where the contract is sealed, only one copy needs to bear the seals.

The contractor should be given in addition, two copies of the unpriced bills, or, if there are no bills, two copies of the specification, and two copies of the drawings, plus two copies of any descriptive schedules or similar documents. If the PQS is responsible for organizing the arrangements for the signing, he will usually collect together beforehand two sets of the documents and hand them to the contractor at the meeting at which the contract is executed.

THE CONTRACT SUM

In the case of a lump sum contract, a specified sum of money is stated in the contract as to be paid by the Employer to the Contractor for the carrying out of the construction work. This sum is seldom, if ever, a fixed amount but is subject to additions and deductions in respect of various matters. Consequently, the JCT Form, in the Articles of Agreement, after providing for the insertion of the contract sum, continues 'or such other sum as shall become payable hereunder at the times and in the manner specified in the Conditions'.

The main causes for adjustment of the contract sum for which the Conditions make provision are: the adjustment of prime cost and provisional sums; variations to the design and/or the specification of the work; additions or reductions to the scope of the work, loss or expense incurred by the contractor for specified reasons and increases or decreases in the costs of labour and materials or in taxes, levies or contributions imposed by Government.

The variable nature of the contract sum may, at first sight, appear to nullify the value of stating any sum at all. It does have the merit, however, of giving the parties a good indication of the level of cost and providing a basis for estimating the eventual cost at later stages in the progress of the project.

The scope for adjustment of the contract sum is not unlimited. Clause 14.2 of the JCT Form limits adjustment to the express provisions of the Conditions of the contract. It specifically excludes the correction of errors made in the contractor's computation of the contract sum.

REFERENCE

1. JCT, *Practice Note 23, A Contract Sum Analysis* (London: RIBA Publications Ltd, 1987).

7

Prime cost and provisional sums

DEFINITIONS

Prime cost (p.c.) sums and provisional sums are lump sums included in the contract sum to cover the cost of parts of the work which are not measured in the bills (in the case of a 'with quantities' contract) or specified in detail in the specification (in the case of a 'without quantities' contract).

A *prime cost sum* is a sum provided for work or services to be executed by a nominated sub-contractor, a statutory authority or a public undertaking or for materials or goods to be obtained from a nominated supplier.

A *provisional sum* is a sum provided for either 'defined' or 'undefined' work. *Defined work* is work which is not completely designed at the time the tender documents are issued but for which certain specified information can be given.[1] *Undefined work* is work for which such specific information cannot be given.

The right to nominate is solely the architect's. He may exercise that right.

(a) by naming a *sub-contractor* or *supplier* in a prime cost sum item in the bills of quantities or specification;

(b) by naming a *supplier* in an architect's instruction relating to the expenditure of a prime cost sum or a provisional sum;

(c) by naming a *sub-contractor* on the Standard Form of Nomination of a Sub-Contractor NSC/3 to carry out work for which a prime cost sum is included in the bills of quantities or specification;

(d) by naming a *sub-contractor* in an architect's instruction issued under clause 35.11.2.

The reasons for dealing with parts of the work by the use of p.c. sums are:

(a) in the case of nominated sub-contractor's work, to give the architect control over the choice of firm to carry out the work, particularly where it is of a specialist nature or outside the scope of work normally carried out by general contractors.

(b) in the case of nominated suppliers' materials or goods, to enable the architect to select articles or materials manufactured by particular firms.

Provisional sums are used where the nature or extent of parts of the work has not been or cannot be ascertained before the construction begins, although such work can be reasonably foreseen as necessary or likely to be necessary. They may also be used to cover certain liabilities, fees or charges which the contractor may have to meet, for example, local authority charges for rates for temporary buildings or for work to be carried out by a local authority or public undertaking. Such costs are often not ascertainable precisely beforehand.

A special kind of provisional sum is one for contingencies, known as a *contingency sum*. This is to meet or offset costs of work or expenses which cannot be foreseen before construction begins and which may not arise at all. A contingency sum has no real relation therefore to the contract works at all and in practice merely serves to reduce the total nett cost of any extra or more expensive work than that originally envisaged.

SUB-CONTRACTS AND CONTRACTS OF SALE

In order to safeguard the rights of the parties in a building project and to make their respective obligations legally binding, a contractor is required to enter into sub-contracts and contracts of sale with nominated sub-contractors and nominated suppliers respectively. So, in relation to sub-contract work, clause 35.3 lists standard forms of tender, nomination, and sub-contract, the use of which constitutes a standard procedure (known as the *basic method* of nomination)[2] described in clauses 35.4 to 35.10.

Clauses 35.11 and 35.12 describe the *alternative method* of nomination for which the JCT issued in September 1986 a similar set of documents: Tender NSC/1a, Nomination Instruction NSC/

3a and Articles of Agreement and Appendix to NSC/4a. These are optional documents additional to Agreement NSC/2a and Nominated Sub-Contract NSC/4a, referred to in clauses 35.11 and 35.12 and published in 1980.

The provisions in clause 36 (Nominated Suppliers) are much simpler. They specify various rights and obligations to be included in a contract of sale, unless the architect and contractor agree otherwise.

It is important, therefore, that the surveyor when dealing with prime cost sums is aware of the agreements which have been entered into by the contractor and must adjust the contract sum accordingly, within the scope and limitations of those agreements.

PRIME COST SUMS

The term *prime cost* has been defined already in Chapter 2 to mean 'the total cost to the contractor of buying materials, goods and components, of using or hiring plant and of employing labour'. In the present context, its meaning is extended to include the cost to the contractor of employing nominated sub-contractors to carry out specified parts of the Works, and the cost of materials and goods obtained from nominated suppliers.

Clauses 35 and 36 of the JCT Form describe the manner in which prime cost sums should be dealt with. Put simply, when the contract sum is adjusted at the end of the contract, the prime cost sums are deducted and the corresponding actual sums expended are substituted. In practice, however, various matters of detail are involved, which must be dealt with properly. These are:

(a) discounts;
(b) nett prices and incorrect discount;
(c) general contractor's profit;
(d) attendances on nominated sub-contractors.

Discounts

Discounts are amounts by which quoted or stated costs or prices may be reduced when paying accounts, usually depending on the fulfilment of specified conditions.

(i) Trade discounts

These discounts are customarily allowed off the prices on standard price lists of materials and goods in particular trades. This is often done to avoid frequent revision of such lists, the discount being varied to allow for fluctuations in prices. In addition, some suppliers will allow larger discounts to regular customers or those who buy large quantities. Contractors may thus obtain more favourable discounts from one merchant than another.

(ii) Cash discounts

These are allowed off invoice prices if the contractor pays within a certain period. In the case of sub-contractors, this period is seventeen days after issue of the architect's certificate which includes the value of the invoiced work or services. In the case of suppliers, the period is thirty days from the end of the month during which delivery of the materials or goods is made. If payment is not made within the specified period, the contractor is not entitled to deduct the discount. As far as the PQS is concerned, however, the amount he allows against the p.c. sum will always include the appropriate cash discount (but see below under 'Nett prices and incorrect discount').

Under the JCT Form, all discounts *except* cash discounts, must be deducted from any sums due to subcontractors and suppliers. In addition, cash discounts in excess of 2½ per cent in the case of nominated subcontractors and 5 per cent in the case of nominated suppliers must also be deducted. This means that the Employer has the benefit of all discounts other than the specified percentages for cash discounts.

Nett prices and incorrect discount

Sometimes sub-contractors and suppliers quote nett prices (that is, prices exclusive of cash discount) or prices inclusive of cash discount but at the wrong percentage. The provisions of the Standard Forms give the contractor the right to the appropriate discount and the Employer the right not to have to pay more than the appropriate discount. They also, in effect, prevent the architect nominating a sub-contractor or supplier who will not allow such discount.

The use of the JCT Standard Form of Nominated Sub-Contract Tender (Tender NSC/1 or NSC/1a) ensures that the discount included in sub-contractors' tenders is correct as it refers specifically on p. 1 to '2½% cash discount allowable to the Main Contractor under Sub-Contract NSC/4'. However, in cases where the basic method of nomination of a sub-contractor is not followed or where Tender NSC/1a is not used under the alternative method of nomination, difficulties in regard to discount may arise and consideration needs to be given to the proper way to deal with them. The following paragraphs relate to the correction of amounts where the proper discount has not been included in tenders or in invoices for sub-contractors' work or suppliers' goods.

The simple solution where quotations or tenders are nett or include the wrong percentage is for the architect to request the sub-contractor or supplier to revise the quotation to include the correct discount. They will usually do so without demur.

If the architect instructs the contractor to place an order against a quotation which includes incorrect discount or no discount at all, the contractor should draw the architect's attention to the error before proceeding. If the contractor places the order without query, he may be deemed to have waived his right to the discount altogether.[3]

It has been argued[4] that, under the JCT Form, if the architect so instructs the contractor then he is acting outside his powers and that the proper course for the contractor is to request the architect, under clause 4.2, to specify under what clause he has issued the Instruction. This course would probably lead to clause 13 being used to provide the due compensation for loss of discount.

In practice, however, things are not always done 'by the book'. The architect may not think it to be worthwhile asking for a revised quotation and the contractor, on his part, may not wish to appear to be challenging the architect. The latter may therefore say to the contractor 'The PQS will allow for the discount in the final account' and will request the PQS so to do. The contractor will usually be disposed to accept this solution to the difficulty. The PQS must then make the appropriate adjustment to the invoice amount when adjusting the p.c. sum.

It should be noted that the effect of dealing with the matter in this way is that the contractor receives a sum equivalent to the discount irrespective of the time of payment of the invoice.

The following examples show the calculations in the more

common cases. Each assumes that the architect instructed the contractor to place an order on the basis of a quotation which included either the wrong discount or no discount, promising that the PQS would adjust for the error in the final account.

Example 1

A nominated sub-contractor rendered an invoice for £6240 for floor tiling supplied and laid, the invoice being marked 'nett, monthly account'.*

The invoice ought to have included 2½ per cent cash discount and to correct the error, $^1/_{39}$th should be added, because the percentages are always deductible from gross (i.e. inclusive) totals.

		£
Correction:	Amount of invoice	6240.00
	Add $^1/_{39}$th	160.00
	Corrected total	6400.00

(*Check*: 2½% of £6400.00 = £160.00.)

The sum of £6 400.00 will be paid by the Employer to the contractor who will retain 2½ per cent of that sum (i.e. £160.00) and pay the balance of £6240.00 to the sub-contractor.

Example 2

A nominated sub-contractor rendered an invoice for £12,480.00 for an electrical installation. The invoice stated '5 per cent cash discount, monthly account'.

The percentage was incorrect and should have been 2½ per cent. The Employer is entitled to receive the benefit of discounts greater than 2½ per cent; consequently, the difference must be deducted to arrive at the proper sum to be paid to the contractor, who may then deduct 2½ per cent as his discount. To correct the total, the incorrect 5 per cent should be deducted and an addition of $^1/_{39}$th made to the resulting nett amount.

*The words 'monthly account' indicate that the credit agreement between contractor and sub-contractor is that credit is given on a monthly basis only.

		£
Correction:	Amount of invoice	12 480.00
	Deduct 5%	624.00
		11 856.00
	Add ¹/₃₉th	304.00
	Corrected total	12 160.00

(*Check*: 2½% of £12 160.00 = £304.00.)

The Employer will pay the contractor £12,160.00 who will then deduct 2½ per cent for cash discount and pay the sub-contractor £11,856.00, which equals the invoice amount less the 5 per cent shown on the invoice.

Example 3

A nominated supplier of ironmongery invoiced the goods supplied at £6 080.76 and marked the invoice 'nett'.

Cash discount should have been included at 5 per cent. ¹/₁₉th should be added in this case to correct the error.

		£
Correction:	Amount of invoice	6080.76
	Add ¹/₁₉th	320.04
	Corrected total	6400.80

(*Check*: 5% of £6400.80 = £320.04.)

Example 4

A nominated supplier of sanitary appliances invoiced goods at £9135.20, the invoice showing cash discount at 2½ per cent instead of 5 per cent. To correct the error, the incorrect 2½ per cent should be deducted and 5 per cent substituted by adding ¹/₁₉th to the nett amount.

		£
Correction:	Amount of invoice	9135.20
	Deduct 2½%	228.38
		8906.82
	Add ¹/₁₉th	468.78
	Corrected total	9375.60

(*Check*: 5% of £9375.60 = £468.78.)

The Employer will pay the contractor £9375.60 who will then deduct his rightful discount of 5 per cent (£468.78) and pay the supplier the balance of £8906.82, which is the sum the latter will expect to be paid having allowed 2½ per cent off the sum invoiced.

Clause 21.3 of the JCT Nominated Sub-Contract NSC/4 gives the contractor the right to deduct 2½ per cent cash discount from *any* sum due to a sub-contractor which is included in the amount of a certificate for payment, if payment is made within the stipulated period of seventeen days. This has sometimes been interpreted as giving the contractor the right to deduct the discount from a nett sum shown on an invoice rendered by a sub-contractor, with whom an order had previously been placed on the basis of a nett quotation.

It should be remembered, however, that those provisions of clause 21.3 which relate to the deduction of cash discount are based on the premise that the architect will have nominated the sub-contractor on the basis of a tender submitted on the JCT Form of Nominated Sub-Contract Tender NSC/1, which specifically refers to allowance made for the discount. Thus the clause does not apply to the situation where a nett quotation has been accepted. In that circumstance, an adjustment of the kind illustrated above would need to be made in order that the provisions of the clause may become effective and the contractor receive the benefit of the discount to which he is entitled.

It should be noted that the stipulated percentages for cash discount apply to the total cost of materials or goods supplied by a nominated supplier (including any tax or duty and the cost of packing, carriage and delivery), and to the total value of sub-contract works (including any dayworks and fluctuations amounts).

Clause 21.4 of the JCT Nominated Sub-Contract NSC/4 requires the addition of one thirty-ninth to fluctuations and certain other costs so that the general contractor can deduct the discount without reducing the original amounts.

It hardly needs saying that if the payment to a sub-contractor is not made by the general contractor at all but direct by the Employer for any reason, then the former is not entitled to cash discount or a sum equivalent to it.

Statutory undertakings (e.g. electricity and gas boards) do not normally give cash discounts. This is recognized in the JCT Form in clause 6.3 by the express exclusion in such cases of the provisions of clause 35, where the work is executed by the statutory undertaker 'solely in pursuance of its statutory obligations'. The fact that the p.c. sums for work or services by statutory undertakers are nett should be made clear in the tender documents. The tenderer is usually told that he will be deemed to have made allowance in the profit addition for any extra amount he may require in lieu of cash discount. In consequence, there will be no need for any adjustment to be made to the nett totals of invoices in the manner illustrated above.

It follows from the wording of clauses 6.2 and 6.3, that where a local authority or statutory undertaker is nominated to carry out works outside the scope of its statutory obligations (e.g. electrical and gas installations in buildings), then it is a nominated subcontractor and the provisions of clause 35 apply, including the discount provisions.

General contractor's profit

Prime cost sums are deemed to be exclusive of the general contractor's profit. Provision is made in bills of quantities and specifications for a separate addition which is normally calculated as a percentage of the p.c. sum, the tenderer stating the percentage that he requires. When the contract sum is adjusted by the omission of p.c. sums and the substitution of actual costs incurred, the profit amounts will also be adjusted *pro rata*, by applying the same percentages to the actual costs as those inserted in the tender document against the respective p.c. sums.

Sometimes the profit additions may be shown as lump sums, without any indication of the method of calculation. In those cases also, such sums should be adjusted *pro rata* to the actual costs.

In the event of the Employer paying a sub-contractor direct for any reason, the general contractor is still entitled to the profit addition, as this is a management fee for arranging, organizing and taking responsibility for the sub-contract or for arranging and checking the supply of goods and materials, as the case may be.

Attendances

A general contractor has to 'attend upon' nominated sub-contractors, as he is responsible for their work and for the integration of the sub-contract works into the main contract works. So, in his own interests, he needs to provide facilities to sub-contractors so that their work may proceed unimpeded. Tenderers are directed in the tender documents to allow for all such attendances in their tender sum.

When there are bills of quantities, 'general attendances' on all nominated sub-contractors are given together in one item; individual items are given for 'special attendances' on each sub-contractor as required. The former are defined in the *Standard Method of Measurement*, clause A42, as 'including the use of Contractor's temporary roads, pavings and paths, standing scaffolding . . . standing power-operated hoisting plant, the provision of temporary lighting and water supplies, clearing away rubbish, provision of space for the sub-contractor's own offices and the storage of his plant and materials and the use of messrooms, sanitary accommodation and welfare facilities provided by the contractor for his own use'.

'Special attendances' include such facilities as scaffolding, access roads and hardstanding additional to that which would otherwise be required, unloading and positioning heavy and large items, storage accommodation and provision of power supplies.

The prices included in tenders for attendances are usually treated as fixed sums which, unlike the profit additions, are not normally adjustable *pro rata* to the actual cost of the sub-contract works. This is because the kind and amount of work or services involved in the attendances remain the same, whether the actual costs are higher or lower than the p.c. sum. Only in the event of the sub-contract works being varied from what was originally envisaged to the extent of affecting the nature or the scope of the attendances, would the attendance amounts be varied.

Sometimes contractors show prices of attendance items as percentages of the p.c. sums in the same way as the profit items. In such cases, the amounts should still be treated as lump sums and the PQS would be wise to obtain the contractor's agreement to this and to the deletion of the percentage rates, prior to the signing of the contract.

EXAMPLES OF ADJUSTMENT OF P.C. AND PROVISIONAL SUMS

The following examples relate to the contract of which particulars are given in Appendix A. The list of p.c. and provisional sums included in the bills of quantities is given on pp. 226 and 227. During the course of the contract, the architect issued Instructions nominating the sub-contractors and requiring orders to be placed with suppliers, as indicated below.

Nominated sub-contractors

Piling

The tender dated 12 January 1987, submitted by Drivas & Co. Ltd, in the sum of £11,340 was accepted in AI No. 1 dated 24 February 1987. Drivas's account dated 26 June 1987 was for the same as quoted, i.e. £11,340.

Asphalt tanking and roofing

The tender dated 3 February 1987 submitted by Asphaltank Ltd, in the sum of £13,725 was also accepted in AI No. 1 dated 24 February 1987. Asphaltank's account dated 3 May 1988 totalled £14,107, made up of £13,725 as quoted, £58 for increased costs of materials, £117 for dayworks resulting from AI No. 10 for alterations to work already executed and £207 for labour costs increases (made up of £201.83 plus one thirty-ninth). The £58 was deducted by the PQS as inadmissible on the ground that asphalt was not on the list of basic prices of materials attached to the tender (see Chapter 9). The amount set against the p.c. sum, therefore, was £14,049.

Electrical installation

The tender dated 10 February 1987 submitted by Sparkes & Co. Ltd, in the sum of £18,000 was accepted and the sub-contractor was nominated in AI No. 1 dated 24 February 1987. Sparkes' account was dated 3 October 1988 and totalled £18,402.30, the extra £402.30 on the quoted amount being for nett labour costs increases plus one thirty-ninth. This total was accepted and set against the p.c. sum.

Lifts installation

The tender dated 26 May 1987 submitted by Wayward Lifts Ltd, in the sum of £33,975 was accepted and the sub-contractor nominated in AI No. 21 dated 3 July 1987. Wayward Lifts submitted an account dated 20 December 1988 which totalled £35,804.79 which included £1152.36 for increases in the cost of steel and £677.43 for labour costs increases (both sums including the addition of one thirty-ninth to the nett amounts). These amounts were accepted, steel being on the list of basic prices of materials attached to the tender.

All the above-mentioned quotations, tenders and accounts showed the correct cash discount.

Nominated suppliers

Kitchen fitments

A quotation dated 9 November 1987 was given by G. F. Joinery Ltd, amounting to £3215. In AI No. 40 dated 16 November 1987, the architect instructed the contractor to place an order in accordance with the quotation. The contractor telephoned the architect on 20 November pointing out that the quotation allowed only 2½ per cent cash discount and the AI was not therefore in accordance with the contract. The architect agreed but said that as there was a delay in delivery of two months at present, it would help if the contractor would place the order and the discount would be allowed for in the settlement of accounts. The contractor agreed to this and placed the order. Delivery of the fitments began in mid-January and was completed in early August. An invoice dated 25 August 1988 was rendered by G. F. Joinery but was endorsed 'nett monthly account'. When the invoice was passed to the PQS, he amended it to read '2½ per cent monthly account' to agree with the quotation and then adjusted the total to £3299.60 as shown in Figure 10, to allow for the correct discount.

Ironmongery

NKG Ltd submitted a quotation dated 13 October 1987 for £2923 and the contractor placed an order accepting it on 9 November 1987, as instructed in AI No. 38 dated 6 November. An account dated 1 May 1988 was rendered which was in accordance with the quotation. A second account dated 4 July 1988 for additional ironmongery ordered on 11 April arising from AI No. 56, totalled

ADJUSTMENT OF PRIME COST AND PROVISIONAL SUMS*

Summary

	Omissions £ p	Additions £ p
Piling	378 00	
Asphalt tanking and roofing	2 258 55	
Electrical installation		422 42
Lifts installation		1 685 03
Kitchen fitments	315 42	
Ironmongery		371 36
Sanitary appliances	391 23	
Water main connection		12 29
Electricity mains connection		21 60
Gas main connection		10 40
Sewer connections		23 81
Rates on temporary buildings		231 25
Telephone for use of Employer	262 43	
Landscaping		341 13
Contingencies	8 000 00	
	11 605 63	3 119 29
Less Additions	3 119 29	
NETT OMISSION CARRIED TO FINAL ACCOUNT	8 486 34	

*The adjustment of provisional sums, if numerous, may be shown separately from p.c. sums.

Piling				
P.c. sum as item 144A		11 700 00		
Profit as item 144B	5%	585 00		
Drivas & Co. Ltd's account date 26/6/87				11 340 00
Profit *pro rata* item 144B			5%	567 00
		12 285 00		11 907 00
Less Additions		11 907 00		
Nett omission carried to Summary		378 00		

Figure 10 Adjustment of prime cost and provisional sums

		Omissions		Additions	
		£	p	£	p
Asphalt tanking and roofing					
P.c. sum as item 144E		16 200	00		
Profit as item 144F	5%	810	00		
Asphaltank Ltd's account dated 3/5/88				14 049	00
Profit *pro rata* item 144F				5% 702	45
		17 010	00	14 751	45
Less Additions		14 751	45		
Nett omission carried to Summary		2 258	55		
Electrical installation					
P.c. sum as item 145A		18 000	00		
Profit as item 145B	5%	900	00		
Sparkes & Co. Ltd's account dated 3/10/88				18 402	30
Profit *pro rata* item 145B				5% 920	12
		18 900	00	19 322	42
Less Omissions				18 900	00
Nett addition carried to Summary				422	42
Lifts					
P.c. sum as item 145E		34 200	00		
Profit as item 145F	5%	1 710	00		
Wayward Lifts Ltd's account dated 20/12/88				35 804	79
Profit *pro rata* item 145F				5% 1 790	24
		35 910	00	37 595	03
Less Omissions				35 910	00
Nett addition carried to Summary				1 685	03
Kitchen fitments					
P.c. sum as item 146A		3 600	00		
Profit as item 146B	5%	180	00		
G. F. Joinery Ltd's invoice dated 25/8/88				3 215	00
Less incorrect cash discount				$2\frac{1}{2}$% 80	38
				3 134	62
Add correct cash discount				$1/19$ 164	98
				3 299	60
Profit *pro rata* item 146B				5% 164	98
		3 780	00	3 464	58
Less Additions		3 464	58		
Nett omission carried to Summary		315	42		

Figure 10   (*cont.*)

		Omissions £ p	Additions £ p
Ironmongery			
P.c. sum as item 146C		2 700 00	
Profit as item 146D	5%	135 00	
NKG Ltd's invoice dated 1/5/88			2 923 00
NKG Ltd's invoice dated 4/7/88			130 68
			3 053 68
Profit *pro rata* item 146D		5%	152 68
		2 835 00	3 206 36
Less Omissions			2 835 00
Nett addition carried to Summary			371 36

Sanitary appliances			
P.c. sum as item 146E		4 320 00	
Profit as item 146F	5%	216 00	
Saniware Ltd's invoice dated 11/5/88			3 947 40
Profit *pro rata* item 146F		5%	197 37
		4 536 00	4 144 77
Less Additions		4 144 77	
Nett omission carried to Summary		391 23	

Water main connection			
P.c. sum as item 146G		360 00	
Profit as item 146H	5%	18 00	
Thames Water Board's account			
dated 21/9/87			371 70
Profit *pro rata* item 146H		5%	18 59
		378 00	390 29
Less Omissions			378 00
Nett addition carried to Summary			12 29

Electricity mains connection			
P.c. sum as item 147A		360 00	
Profit as item 147B	5%	18 00	
South Eastern Electricity Board's account			
dated 13/10/87			380 57
Profit *pro rata* item 147B		5%	19 03
		378 00	399 60
Less Omissions			378 00
Nett addition carried to Summary			21 60

Figure 10 (*cont.*)

		Omissions		Additions	
		£	p	£	p
Gas main connection					
P.c. sum as item 147D		540	00		
Profit as item 147E	5%	27	00		
South Eastern Gas Board's account					
dated 2/11/87				549	90
Profit *pro rata* item 147E				5%	27 50
		567	00	577	40
Less Omissioris				567	00
Nett addition carried to Summary				10	40
Sewer connections					
P.c. sum as item 147G		900	00		
Profit as item 147H	5%	45	00		
Urbiston Borough Council's account					
dated 2/10/87				922	68
Profit *pro rata* item 147H				5%	46 13
		945	00	968	81
Less Omissions				945	00
Nett addition carried to Summary				23	81
Rates on temporary buildings					
Provisional sum as item 147K		2 000	00		
Urbiston Borough Council's					
accounts dated 1/3/88				1 250	00
1/12/88				875	00
				2 125	00
Profit				5%	106 25
		2 000	00	2 231	25
Less Omissions				2 000	00
Nett addition carried to Summary				231	25

Figure 10   *(cont.)*

	Omissions £ p		Additions £ p	
Telephone for use of Employer				
Provisional sum as item 147L	750	00		
British Telecom accounts dated				
10/6/87			185	26
9/9/87			42	15
11/12/87			40	32
9/3/88			58	76
13/6/88			52	40
7/9/88			49	34
14/12/88			36	12
			464	35
Profit 5%			23	22
	750	00	487	57
Less Additions	487	57		
Nett omission carried to Summary	262	43		
Landscaping				
Provisional sum as item 147M	2 250	00		
Surrey Landscapes Ltd's account				
dated 30/11/88			2 372	50
Profit 5%			118	63
General attendance			100	00
	2 250	00	2 591	13
Less Omissions			2 250	00
Nett addition carried to Summary			341	13
Contingencies				
Provisional sum as item 147K	8 000	00		
Nett omission carried to Summary	8 000	00		

Figure 10   *(cont.)*

£130.68. Both accounts were in order and included the correct discount.

Sanitary appliances

Saniware Ltd quoted on 3 July 1987 for sanitary appliances for the sum of £3924.90. This was accepted on 27 July 1987, as AI No. 25 dated 21 July. Saniware Ltd's invoice dated 11 May 1988 totalled £3947.40, made up of the sum quoted plus £22.50 for special packings, and this was accepted by the PQS.

Statutory bodies

The architect issued AI No. 2 on 3 March 1987 instructing the contractor to place orders with the Water, Electricity and Gas Boards and with Urbiston Borough Council for sewer connections. The work was carried out and, in due course, accounts were received as follows, each account demanding payment in full, and being marked 'Nett'.

Water main connection

Thames Water Board's account dated 21 September 1987 was for £371.70.

Electricity mains connection

South Eastern Electricity Board's account dated 13 October 1987 was for £380.57.

Gas main connection

South Eastern Gas Board's account was dated 2 November 1987 and was for £549.90.

Sewer connections

The Urbiston Borough Council's account was dated 2 October 1987 and was for £922.68.

Rates on temporary buildings

Two accounts were received from Urbiston Borough Council dated 1 March 1988 and 1 December 1988 for £1250 and £875 respectively.

Telephone for use of Employer

Accounts were received from British Telecom at quarterly intervals between June 1987 and December 1988, the first of which included the installation charge.

Landscaping

The architect instructed the contractor in AI No. 84 dated 1 September 1988 to place an order with Surrey Landscapes Ltd for landscape work in accordance with their quotation dated 26 August 1988 in the sum of £2372.50. Their account dated 30 November 1988 was for that amount. Profit was added at the same rate (5 per cent) as was included in the bills for other nominated sub-contracts. General attendance was added at an agreed amount (£100).

Figure 10 shows a method of presenting the adjustment of p.c. and provisional sums in accordance with the foregoing data. An alternative format is preferred by some PQSs which differs from that given in the example, in that the total omission and total addition relative to each p.c. sum are carried over to the Summary and then the nett omission or nett addition is calculated from the totals. Figure 11 shows what the Summary looks like when using this alternative format. The first alternative has the advantage that the nett saving or extra resulting from the adjustment of each p.c. sum is shown. If this additional information is not of any particular use, then it does not matter which method is used.

GENERAL CONTRACTOR CARRYING OUT WORKS COVERED BY P.C. SUMS

A general contractor may wish to carry out work himself for which a p.c. sum has been included in the contract documents or which has arisen under an AI. The JCT Form provides for this in clause

ADJUSTMENT OF PRIME COST AND PROVISIONAL SUMS*

Summary

	Omissions £ p	Additions £ p
Piling	12 285 00	11 907 00
Asphalt tanking and roofing	17 010 00	14 751 45
Electrical installation	18 900 00	19 322 42
Lifts installation	35 910 00	37 595 03
Kitchen fitments	3 780 00	3 464 58
Ironmongery	2 835 00	3 206 36
Sanitary appliances	4 536 00	4 144 77
Water main connection	378 00	390 29
Electricity mains connection	378 00	399 60
Gas main connection	567 00	577 40
Sewer connections	945 00	968 81
Rates on temporary buildings	2 000 00	2 231 25
Telephone for use of Employer	750 00	487 57
Landscaping	2 250 00	2 591 13
Contingencies	8 000 00	–
	110 524 00	102 037 66
Less Additions	102 037 66	
Nett omission carried to final account Summary	8 486 34	

*The adjustment of Provisional sums, if numerous, may be shown separately from p.c. sums.

Figure 11   Adjustment of prime cost and provisional sums: summary by alternative format

35.2, but with limitations. The limitations imposed by the JCT Form are:

(*a*) the work must be such as the general contractor does directly in the normal course of his business, although if he is allowed to do the work he may sub-let it, provided the architect agrees;

(*b*) the contractor must have given notice, prior to the drawing-up of the contract, that he wishes to carry out such work, indicating what the items of work are, so that they may be set out in the Appendix to the Conditions. (If a p.c. sum has arisen because of an AI, then the notice should be given as soon as the AI is received.)

(*c*) the architect must be willing to accept a tender from the contractor for such work; if not, the contractor will not be permitted to do the work himself. Such a refusal will usually be due to the architect preferring a specialist sub-contractor to do it, in whom he has more confidence to provide a satisfactory standard of work.

When the general contractor is permitted to submit a tender and his tender is accepted, the question then arises as to whether he is entitled to be paid the profit addition included in the contract sum. The answer appears to be that it depends on whether the tender for the sub-contract works was submitted in competition or not. If it were, then the general contractor is entitled to the profit addition just as if a sub-contractor were to do the work. If it were not in competition, then the contractor's price should include the full amount of profit, so that, in effect, the p.c. sum is converted into a provisional sum and the contractor should be asked to include in his tender the total amount of profit required.

A general contractor cannot attend upon himself and so, any sum included in the contract sum for general attendance will be deducted. 'Special attendances' (see p. 84) are rather different, since they may involve extra expense such as providing special scaffolding or staging or special plant. If the general contractor tenders in competition with sub-contractors, he would be at a disadvantage if he had to include such extra costs, whereas they would not do so. In those circumstances, the amounts in the contract sum for the relevant items of 'Special attendances' would stand. If the tender is not in competition, the contractor should be instructed to include for all 'attendances' in his tender and any attendance amounts included in the contract sum should be deducted.

A situation which may arise, involving a desire by the general contractor to do sub-contract work himself, is where a nominated sub-contractor defaults before completion of his sub-contract. The general contractor may want to avoid the delay which would be occasioned by the need for the architect to re-nominate, so that the rest of the work may not be held up.

The JCT Form, 1963 Edition, made no direct provision for dealing with this situation. It is not surprising therefore, that this has been the subject of legal action. The classic case is *North-West Metropolitan Hospital Board v. T. A. Bickerton Ltd (1970) 1 All ER 1039*. The House of Lords expressed the view in this case that the general contractor did not have the right (nor the duty) to do work for which p.c. sums had been included in the contract documents.

This appears to conflict with the express provisions of clause 35.2 discussed above but, presumably, this (or more correctly, the corresponding clause 27 (g) in the 1963 Edition, then in force) was outside the scope of the circumstances of the case being considered by the House of Lords and thus was excepted from their Lordships' expressed view. It was also held that, if a nominated sub-contractor defaults, a re-nomination by the architect must follow.

The particular point for the quantity surveyor to note is their Lordships' view that the total cost of the sub-contract works in such circumstances is the responsibility of the Employer, even though it may have been increased due to a new sub-contractor requiring to be paid more to finish the work than it would have cost had the original sub-contractor completed. The case has been discussed at length elsewhere.[4]

The 1980 Edition of the JCT Form, however, does deal with the matter of re-nomination by the architect. The provisions of clause 35.24 were no doubt introduced as a consequence of the *Bickerton* judgment. Briefly, the clause requires the architect to make a further nomination of a sub-contractor to finish the sub-contract works whenever a nominated sub-contractor fails to complete. Any additional expense arising as a consequence is recoverable by the Employer from the contractor, who in turn may be able to recover from the sub-contractor, depending on the cause of the determination of the sub-contract.

PROVISIONAL SUMS

Provisional sums are usually intended to meet the cost of work not determined or defined at the time of tendering, but which normally will be carried out by the general contractor. In due course, the architect will issue, in accordance with clause 13.3 of the JCT Form, written instructions to the contractor from time to time as to what work he is required to do, which will be paid for out of the Provisional sums.

When the contract sum is adjusted at the end of the contract, the Provisional sums, like p.c. sums, will be deducted and the total value of the work actually carried out will be substituted. In order to ascertain what that total cost is, the work will be measured and valued as executed and will be priced in the same way as varied work is priced (see Chapter 8). Such total cost may also include work valued as daywork. Alternatively, the contractor may be asked to submit a tender for carrying out the work and, if his tender is accepted, the amount tendered will be set against the appropriate Provisional sum in the settlement of the accounts.

As the work covered by Provisional sums will normally be carried out by the general contractor and not by a sub-contractor, no items of profit or attendances are attached to such sums in the bills of quantities. The valuation of the work carried out is inclusive of profit and as sub-contractors are not ·normally involved, the question of attendances does not arise.

However, the work for which a Provisional sum has been provided may, if the architect so decides, be carried out not by the general contractor but by a sub-contractor nominated by the architect (*see* clause 35.1.2). Then, the sub-contractor's account will be dealt with in the same way as in the case of a p.c. sum. An item of profit will be added at the percentage rate used for the profit items on p.c. sums for sub-contractors' work in the bills and attendance items, as appropriate, will also be added. Thus, the total of the sub-contractor's account (as submitted or as amended) plus profit and attendance amounts, will be set against the Provisional sum in the final account.

Again, the architect may wish to nominate a particular supplier to supply materials or goods which are to form part of the work for which a Provisional sum has been included in the contract sum. In this case, the contractor will be entitled to a profit addition on the value of the nominated supplier's invoice at the percentage rate of the profit items on comparable p.c. sums in the bills. The remainder of the work will be measured and valued in the same way as varied work, including items for fixing the goods supplied by the nominated supplier.

It should be noted that the situations described in the last two paragraphs are envisaged in clauses 13.3, 35.1.2 and 36.1.2 of the JCT Form. Examples of the adjustment of provisional sums are included in Figure 10.

The question has been raised[5] as to the correct procedure where the actual value of work which is the subject of a Provisional sum exceeds the amount of that sum. In practice, that situation is usually dealt with simply by a nett addition to the contract sum of the excess amount. Where the excess is large, however, a contractor might be disposed to claim an extension of time under clause 25 and reimbursement of any additional loss or expense under clause 13.5.6 on the grounds put forward in the article referred to.

REFERENCES

1. *Standard Method of Measurement of Building Works, Seventh Edition* (London: RICS, 1988), p. 14.
2. *JCT Guide* (London: RIBA Publications Ltd, 1989).
3. POWELL-SMITH, VINCENT, *Contractors' Guide to the JCT's Standard Forms of Building Contract* (Sutton: IPC Building & Contract Journals Ltd, 1977), p. 24.
4. ibid., p. 24.
5. SIMS, J. Sims on Contract Practice, *Building*, 1974, Vol. 227, No. 49, p. 98.

8

Variations

DEFINITION AND ORIGIN OF VARIATIONS

The definition of the term 'variation' in clause 13.1 of the JCT Form indicates the wide scope for the exercise of the architect's power to vary the Works.

Variations may arise in any of the following situations (references are to the JCT Form):

(a) when the architect needs or wishes to vary the design or the specification;

(b) when a discrepancy is discovered between any two or more of the contract documents (*see* clause 2.3);

(c) when a discrepancy is discovered between any statutory requirement and any of the contract documents (*see* clause 6.1);

(d) when an error in or omission from the contract bills is discovered (*see* clause 2.2).

By far the largest number of variations arises under (a). In cases (a), (b) and (c), the architect is required to issue instructions but that is not necessary in the case of (d). All such instructions must be in writing. Consequently, although the architect may order any variation that he wishes, the contractor is bound to carry out such an order only if it is in the form of a written instruction issued by the architect. If the contractor carries out any variation involving him in additional expense, and the variation has not been the subject of a written Architect's Instruction (AI), he runs the risk of being unable to recover the extra costs.

The contractor is safeguarded, however, in the event of instructions being given orally. Under clause 4.3 of the JCT Form, an oral instruction 'shall be confirmed in writing by the contractor to the architect within seven days'. The architect has the opportunity during seven days following receipt of that confirmation to dissent, otherwise the instruction becomes effective immediately. Failing such action, the architect may issue a confirmation at any later time but prior to the issue of the Final Certificate. Where oral instructions have allegedly been given and complied with but not subsequently confirmed, some PQSs ask the architect to issue confirmation, if he is willing to do so.

The architect may thus issue a written instruction which sanctions a variation already carried out in compliance with oral instructions. Clause 13.2 of the JCT Form goes further, enabling the architect to sanction subsequently any variation which a contractor has already carried out not in pursuance of an AI, oral or written.

On contracts where there is a clerk of works, any directions which he may properly give to the contractor (whether orally or in writing) become effective only if confirmed in writing by the architect within two working days (clause 12).

It is necessary, therefore, for the PQS to satisfy himself, before giving financial effect to any variation, that written instructions have been given by the architect, ordering or sanctioning the variation, or if the contractor claims to have confirmed oral instructions, that the architect does not dissent from such confirmation. The PQS has no authority to adjust the Contract Sum in respect of a variation which has not been put into the form of a written AI or been otherwise confirmed in writing (*see* comment on p. 5).

It should be appreciated that all Architect's Instructions do not necessarily constitute or contain variations to the contract. Some may be explanatory, others may direct how provisional sums and p.c. sums are to be expended, yet others may instruct the contractor to remove from the site materials not in accordance with the contract. None of these AIs may constitute a variation to the Works.

The cause of a variation listed as (*d*) above arises under clause 2.2 of the JCT Form. This is where an error or omission has occurred in the compilation by the PQS of the bills of quantities upon which a contract sum has been based. In such circumstances the error or omission must be rectified and 'shall be treated as if it were a variation'. It should be noted that this does *not* relate to errors made by the contractor when pricing bills of quantities (see p. 56).

MEASURING VARIATIONS

Few, if any, variations have no effect on the Contract Sum. In order, therefore, to adjust the Contract Sum adequately and satisfactorily within the Conditions of the contract, the PQS (and the contractor's surveyor, too, if he wishes) must ascertain the nett extra cost or nett saving involved. To do that, the affected work will have to be measured, except in those instances where the method of valuation makes it unnecessary, as discussed below. This means that the work originally designed, which will not be required as a consequence of the variation, must be identified, isolated and valued, and that which will be required to replace the omitted work must be measured and valued. Such measurement may be done from drawings or, if drawings are not available, by physically measuring the substituted work on the site after it has been carried out.

This same procedure will be necessary whether the contract is based upon bills of firm quantities or on specification and drawings only. In the case of contracts based upon bills of approximate quantities and those based on a schedule of rates, the whole of the Works will have to be measured as described above. In all cases the valuing will be done in the manner discussed in the section below headed 'Valuing variations'.

It should be appreciated that in the case of 'without quantities' contracts, the work omitted will have to be measured in detail, as well as the substituted work, there being no simple procedure of identifying bill items affected, as in the case of 'with quantities' contracts. Where there are bills, it will often be necessary to refer back to the original dimension sheets in order to identify exactly what was included in the bills for the work which has been varied. If the items affected constitute complete bill items, they can be identified by their item references either as a single item or a group of items, e.g. 'item 132B' or 'items 132B-G'. If a variety of items is involved, many of which are not complete bill items, the omissions can be identified by reference to the dimension column numbers, e.g. 'original dimensions, X-X cols. 95–103', the letter 'X' being written on the dimension sheets to indicate the commencement and end of the omitted work. The measurement of AIs Nos. 8

and 48 in the examples at the end of the chapter illustrates the alternative procedures.

The PQS has the duty laid upon him by clause 13.6 of the JCT Form, to provide the opportunity for the contractor to be present when measurements of variations are taken. Although the clauses do not specifically refer solely to measurements on site, in practice the provision is not normally applied to measurement from drawings done in the office. It does mean, however, that the PQS must give the contractor's surveyor sufficient notice for him to be able to make arrangements to attend on site when measuring is to be done there.

When measuring on site, it should be remembered that it is intended by the Committee that prepared the Standard Method of Measurement that the rules of measurement in that document should apply equally to measurement on site and to measurement from drawings.[1] This is important, for example, when measuring excavation involving working space and earthwork support. The SMM requires these items to be measured, even though the surveyor doing site measuring may know that they have not actually been done. The dimensions of the excavation should be those which are minimum for the required construction, measured in accordance with the rules of the SMM, notwithstanding that the contractor may have excavated wider to avoid the use of earthwork supports or because the excavator bucket available was wider than needed. So, too, the lengths of timbers whose ends are not cut square (e.g. rafters) should be measured their extreme lengths and inflexible floor tiles (e.g. quarry tiles) should be measured *between* skirtings, particularly where the latter are coved, and not between wall faces.

Measurements taken on site are normally entered in bound dimension books, which consist of pages with dimension column rulings similar to 'cut and shuffle' slips, or to traditional dimension paper but with only one set of columns instead of two. Alternatively, one may use normal dimension paper on a clip board which, although not so convenient to handle as a dimension book, does give the advantage of having all the measurements, whether taken on site or in the office, on the same size sheets.

Another way of dealing with both the measurements and the working-up involved, is to use A4 size paper ruled with dimension columns on the left and quantity and money columns on the right – i.e. similar to estimating paper. Thus, all the information –

measurements, billing and pricing – is presented on the same sheets.

VARIATION ACCOUNTS

When the measurement has been done, the dimensions have to be worked up into variation accounts, which, in compliance with clause 30.6.1.2 of the JCT Form, should be completed and priced and a copy supplied to the contractor not later than 9 months after Practical Completion. In practice, this is seldom achieved. Nevertheless, the PQS should do his best to complete the variation accounts by the expiry of the period stated in the contract as the Employer is in breach of contract if he does not do so.

The format in which the variation accounts are drawn up varies between one firm of PQSs and another. Some firms bill omissions and additions under each AI separately. Others combine all the omissions together and all the additions together, each group being classified under appropriate Work Section headings. The merit of the former method is that the cost of each variation is apparent, together with separate totals of omissions and additions. The main disadvantage is that the variation accounts are almost certain to form a thicker document due to the repetition of items in different variations and also because of the extra space taken up with separate totals. The second method results in less items and a more compact document which takes less time to prepare and price. If all that is required is the amount of the nett extra or saving, then the latter format would seem to be adequate. If details of the costs of the individual variations is needed or desired, then the former method of presentation will probably be necessary. Apart from that, the format may be dictated by custom in individual quantity surveying organizations.

VALUING VARIATIONS

There are several ways of valuing variations, the choice in a particular case being that which is appropriate to the circumstances. They are:

(a) by the inclusion in the variation accounts of a lump sum in accordance with a quotation submitted by the contractor and accepted by the architect;

(*b*) by pricing measured items in the variation accounts;

(*c*) by ascertaining the total prime cost of additional work and applying appropriate percentage additions.

It should be noted that clause 13.4.1.1 of the JCT Form lays the duty of valuing variations upon the PQS, who has the right to decide which is the appropriate method and means of valuing them in each situation. Therefore, he is not bound to accept a statement on an AI to the effect that a variation is 'to be carried out on daywork' or 'to be paid as daywork'. In any case, such a statement may be contrary to the provisions of the JCT Form.

The alternative valuation methods listed above merit further discussion as follows.

Contractor's accepted quotation

The standard forms of contract do not apparently give the architect the authority to use this method, although the words 'unless otherwise agreed' in clause 13.4.1.1 of the JCT Form may be construed as permitting it. In practice, the method is not infrequently used. It is an attractive way of determining a price for a variation because it eliminates the need for time-consuming measurement and pricing. It contains the conditions for inflated prices, however – no competition, possibly pressure of time and also the architect's understandable anxiety to avoid delay. Provided the architect consults the PQS and the latter provides an approximate estimate of *nett* extra cost (i.e. taking account of omissions as well as additions), and the contractor's price bears a reasonable relationship to the estimate, then the danger will be minimized. The possibility should be guarded against of the contractor quoting only for the extra work and the PQS assuming the quotation to allow for omissions as well. Also, such quotations should be invited and given on the clearly-stated basis of inclusion of all overhead costs and profit.

Pricing measured items

The JCT Form in clause 13 is explicit about the way measured items (omissions as well as additions) should be priced. The prices (in particular, unit rates) in the bills or schedule of rates, as the case may be, are to be used. This is subject to the proviso that the character of the work and the conditions of its execution are similar to that in the project as originally envisaged. This covers the pricing of all (or most) omissions and much of the additions (although some omission items in 'without quantities' contracts may not coincide with items in the submitted schedule of rates).

Other items will bear no relationship or comparison at all with items in the contract bills, or may not be carried out under similar conditions to apparently similar items in the bills. In these cases, a 'fair valuation' is to be made. This means that a unit rate may have to be built up from the prime cost of the necessary materials and using labour constants valued at 'all-in' labour rates and with any appropriate allowances for plant and with additions for overheads and profit. If an item is a common one or of small total value, the PQS's knowledge of prices will usually enable him to put a fair price to it without the necessity for a detailed synthesis on the lines just described.

In between the two foregoing groups of items, there is a third group in which the items are not exactly the same as but bear a fairly close resemblance to items in the bills or schedule of rates. These should be priced *on the basis of* the prices of the comparable items. That means in effect, that the pricing of such items is to be done, as far as possible, at the same general level of prices as is contained in the contract documents. Again, where an item of work is common or relatively inexpensive, the PQS will usually be able to 'assess' a comparable rate to the similar bill or schedule item. Where the item is an expensive one in total cost terms, or where there is any dispute, it may be necessary to analyse the contract rate and then to synthesize the new rate on the basis of the analysis. In any case, the student should be able to do price analysis and synthesis and the examples at the end of the chapter will illustrate the process.

Perhaps it should be emphasized that in practice, it is only necessary for relatively few items in variation accounts to be priced by a process of analysis and synthesis. It should be realized, however, that, in theory, the same process is being carried out when a comparable rate is 'assessed'. As in many fields, experience enables one to short-circuit longer procedures, but this can only be done safely, once the underlying principles and procedures have been fully understood and appreciated. Then, (to give a simple illustration) the student will know that a 100 mm thick concrete slab should not be priced at half the price of a 200 mm one to the same specification, even if he still lacks the experience to be able immediately to suggest a reasonable price for the thinner slab.

Prime cost plus percentage additions

This method of valuing variations is commonly known as *daywork* and bears a close resemblance to the valuation of work under the prime cost or cost reimbursement type of contract (see p. 16). Daywork is a method of payment by the reimbursement to the contractor of the prime cost of all materials, labour and plant used in the carrying out of the work, with a percentage addition to the total cost of each of those groups for overheads and profit.

Daywork is subject to the same objection as that levied against prime cost contracts, namely, that its use generally results in higher costs to the Employer than when a 'measure and value' basis is used. Not surprisingly, therefore, daywork is favoured by contractors and deprecated by the Employer's professional advisers.

This generally acknowledged characteristic of daywork is the reason for the restriction of its use in the Standard Forms to situations where 'work cannot properly be valued by measurement'. This provision should be strictly observed in the Employer's interest. If work is capable of adequate measurement, it can usually also be priced using unit rates determined as described under *Pricing measured items* above.

Such measurement must be capable of being 'properly' done, which would exclude, for example, measuring some alteration or adaptation works by a single 'number item' with a long and complicated description, merely to avoid paying the contractor daywork. In any case, to price such an item would probably involve the PQS in asking the contractor how long had been spent on the work, what materials and how much of them had been used, and what plant – which comes down to something very much like daywork in the end! The PQS should recognize and accept that the contractor has the right to be paid on a daywork basis where appropriate and that the Employer has the right to pay on a measured basis where that can reasonably be done.

As with prime cost contracts, it is necessary to have a precise definition of what is included in the prime cost in each of its three divisions – materials, labour, and plant. The JCT Form refers to the document *'Definition of Prime Cost of Daywork carried out under a Building Contract'*[2] as the basis to be used for the calculation of the prime cost, or, in the case of specialist work, a comparable document appropriate to that work, if one exists.

The respective percentages to be added to the totals of each section of the prime cost will be those included in the contract document, i.e. bills of quantities or schedule of rates. If by some oversight, no percentages were included, then they would have to be agreed between the PQS and the contractor's surveyor.

The contractor is required to submit 'vouchers' (commonly called 'daywork sheets') not later than the end of the week following that in which the daywork was completed, giving full details of labour, materials and plant used in carrying it out. These vouchers should be verified by the architect or his authorized representative. If there is a clerk of works, he can usually be relied upon to do the verifying. The PQS may be prepared to accept unverified daywork sheets where he is able to satisfy himself that the claim is reasonable, but to do so is not strictly within the terms of the Standard Forms. However, if unverified sheets are accepted and the hours and quantities shown on them are considered to be excessive, the PQS should reduce them to reasonable amounts.

It should be noted that a signature denoting verification by the architect or his representative relates only to the materials used and the time spent[3] and not to the correctness or otherwise of any prices included. The proper valuation is for the PQS to determine.

There are difficulties associated with verifying daywork vouchers but as they are problems for the architect rather than the quantity surveyor, it is not considered necessary to discuss them here; the reader is referred to a relevant article in *Building*.[4]

The rates and prices used for valuing daywork should be those current at the time the work was carried out, not those current at the date of tender. This is so that the application of the respective percentage additions for overheads and profit will be to the total costs. If the rates and prices current at the date of tender were used, the total payment for the daywork would be less (assuming some increases in costs since the tender date). The difference would not be made up by the reimbursement of such increases under the fluctuations provisions of the contract, even if such provisions were included. It is also because rates and prices current at the time the daywork was carried out are used for valuing it, that the value of such work is excluded from the provisions relating to fluctuations in clauses 38, 39 and 40 of the JCT Form.[5]

The rates of labour used in valuing daywork should be standard hourly base rates, irrespective of the actual rates paid. Where rates above the basic rates are paid, the excess comes out of the percentage addition. The method of computing standard hourly base rates for use in pricing dayworks is illustrated on p. 8 of the *Definition of Prime Cost of Daywork*.*

Plant costs may be calculated on the basis of the *Schedule of Basic Plant Charges* issued by the Royal Institution of Chartered Surveyors and intended to be used solely for that purpose. If so, then the rates quoted will require updating. This may be done by a percentage addition before the appropriate percentage for overheads and profit is added, or by combining a suitable updating percentage with that for overheads and profit. Provision for both the use of the *Schedule* and for updating the rates ought to have been made in the contract bills or schedule of rates, as the case may be.

Figure 17 gives an example of a daywork sheet and Figure 16 shows the same information converted into a daywork account for incorporation into a variation account.

ADDITIONAL EXPENSE ARISING FROM VARIATIONS

There is a possibility that the contractor may not always be adequately remunerated for what he is required to do in regard to variations under the terms of the Standard Forms. For example, a variation which increased the width of a number of windows might be ordered. The timing of the order might result in the contractor having bought lintels for the window openings which had been delivered before the variation was ordered, and which, in consequence, became surplus to requirements. The normal measurement of the omissions and additions involved would result in the omission of the shorter lintels and the addition of longer ones and no account would be taken of the surplus lintels. The possibility of additional expense arising from variations is recognized by the JCT Form in clause 13.5.6. The contractor should make a written application to the architect for reimbursement of the additional expense which he has incurred and upon

*For an updated version of the base rate computation, see BCIS *Guide to Daywork Rates*.[6]

receipt of such application if it is justified, the PQS must ascertain the amount involved, which then must be added to the Contract Sum. Any such amount should also be included in the next interim certificate issued under clause 30.

USE OF ERRONEOUS RATES WHEN PRICING VARIATIONS

Sometimes, a rate against a measured item in bills of quantities or in a schedule of rates is inadvertently underpriced or overpriced by the contractor and the error may have escaped the notice of the PQS when examining the tender document before the contract was let, so that nothing was done about it (see p. 55). If subsequently, the item is involved in a variation, then a difficulty may arise in the use of the erroneous rate, which must be resolved.

Suppose, for example, that an item of 'two-coat plaster on walls not exceeding 150 mm wide' had been priced at £0.69 per m^2, (i.e. as if the item were linear instead of superficial). The intended rate should have been £4.55 per m^2. No problem need arise over omissions, as the omitted quantity should, without doubt, be priced at the bill rate. But suppose the additions involve a much larger quantity than that omitted. At what rate should the addition quantity be priced? Is it inequitable to the contractor to price it at the underpriced rate? Is the Employer taking unfair advantage of a genuine error on the contractor's part?

The answers to these questions should be sought by asking 'what does the contract say?'. The JCT Form in clause 13.5.1 clearly states that bill rates shall be used, provided the work is of similar character and executed under similar conditions. There is no authority therefore for the PQS to use a different rate, so long as the work is 'similar' in those respects. As in other aspects of contractual agreements, what has been freely agreed by both parties is binding upon them, notwithstanding that a term of a contract may subsequently prove to be disadvantageous to one of the parties. It seems clear, therefore, that the contractor must stand the loss (or be allowed to gain the benefit, as the case may be) of an erroneously-priced item that is involved in variations.

A compromise that has been suggested from time to time is that the erroneous rate should be applied only up to the limit of the quantity of the item in the contract bills to which it applies and that beyond that limit a fair rate should be substituted. This will appear to many people as an equitable solution although it must be said again that there is no direct authority in the JCT Form for so doing. The judgment in a case heard in the High Court in 1967, *Dudley Corporation v Parsons & Morris Ltd*, held that the total quantity of an item in a remeasurement should be priced at the erroneous rate in question, a decision which was upheld in the Court of Appeal in 1969. This appears to settle the matter.

The question has been raised whether, in these circumstances, the contractor can justifiably claim reimbursement of the loss resulting from applying the erroneous rate to the additions quantity, under the provision of clause 13.5.6 of the JCT Form. Legal opinion that such a loss could not be recovered under clause 11(6) of the 1963 Edition of the JCT Form[7] would seem to apply also under clause 13.5.6 of the 1980 Edition.

ADJUSTMENT OF PRELIMINARIES ON ACCOUNT OF VARIATIONS

This matter has always been a cause for contention and disagreement. Some contractor's surveyors have argued that if the value of the job is increased by variations, then the Preliminaries should also be increased in proportion, on the grounds that, by and large, they are directly affected by the size and value of the contract.

On the other hand, some PQSs have contended that the Preliminaries should only be adjusted in very exceptional circumstances, i.e. when the size and scope of the job is significantly affected, as, for example, by the addition of another storey or another wing or block. Others have taken the intermediate position that if there has been an extension of time granted in respect of variations, then there may be grounds for adjusting part of the value of Preliminaries.

Editions of the JCT Form published before 1980 were of little or no help in providing a solution, as they made no specific reference to Preliminaries. The 1980 Edition, however, is specific on the matter in clause 13.5.3.3. This requires that, when valuing additional, omitted or substituted work, allowance is to be made for any addition to or reduction of preliminary items. It should be noted, however, that the provision relates only to work 'which can properly be valued by measurement' and so excludes other work, such as daywork. Also excluded is work pursuant to an AI for expenditure of a provisional sum for 'defined work'.

If the PQS has to ascertain the value of any addition to or reduction of Preliminaries, how may he do so? He will first have to satisfy himself as to the proper total value of the Preliminaries. If there are bills of quantities and the Preliminaries are fully priced, the total value is apparent. If, however, they are not fully priced, an assessment of their full value will need to be made, because the JCT Form requires allowance to be made for additions to or reduction of the items. In order to make such allowance, the value of the items as originally intended needs to be known.

In the case of contracts on a 'without quantities' basis, the contract sum will need to be apportioned to its principal constituents, of which the Preliminaries form one, unless a Contract Sum Analysis has already been provided. When the total value of the Preliminaries has been determined, the PQS must then ascertain the value of the individual items which comprise that part of the Contract Sum. Then he will be in a position to proceed with his valuation of any addition or reduction, as the case may be.

If an extension of time has been granted by the architect on account of variations, then those Preliminary items with a time-related content may be considered as ranking for a proportionate increase in that content, whilst the cost-related and lump sum elements remain unchanged.

If no extension has been granted, there may still be justifiable grounds for adjusting the item prices. For example, a variation might result in plant being kept on site longer than otherwise envisaged or in additional supervision being required for the period during which the variation is being carried out. In such situations, the actual expense would need to be ascertained, which would require the assistance of the contractor in providing the necessary details.

It should be appreciated, however, that in no case should the total value of the Preliminaries be increased (or decreased) simply in proportion to the total value of variations. Any adjustment must be made with regard to the amount by which individual Preliminary items have been affected by variations.

EXAMPLES OF VARIATIONS

The following is a list of the first six variations contained in Architect's Instructions issued for the contract of which particulars are given in Appendix A. (AIs not included in the list were those giving instructions regarding the expenditure of p.c. sums and dealing with other matters which did not constitute variations).

AI No.	*Subject of variation*
8	Willingdon Light Buff Facing Bricks in lieu of Hildon Tudor Brown Facing Bricks.
15	The roof slabs to the flats increased from 125 mm thick to 175 mm and the main reinforcement increased from 12 mm to 16 mm diameter
23	Living room windows in flats to be 1800 × 1500 mm in lieu of 1800 × 1200 mm.
28	Glazed screens to balconies to be glazed with pattern group 2 glass with putty in lieu of clear glass in beads.
41	Window removed from existing store, opening in wall altered as necessary, provision of door and frame complete with deadlock, handles and closer.
48	Omission of built-in bookcase units in living rooms.

Figures 12–18 show the taking-off and billing for the variations. The work was billed direct from the taking-off in the case of AIs Nos. 8 and 48. The other AIs illustrate the use of 'estimating paper' ruling as an alternative format.

The following is a commentary on the examples.

AI No. 8 Facing Bricks

This variation was necessitated by Hildon Brickworks Ltd ceasing the manufacture of Tudor Brown Facings. The *additions* items were all the same as the corresponding bill items apart from the change in bricks. As the latter were comparable in type and quality with those originally specified, the rates were adjusted merely to take account of the increased prime cost of the bricks, the value of the other materials and labour being unchanged. The price of the Hildon Tudor Brown Facings used by the contractor when pricing the bills was £176.50 per 1000 including delivery. The price of the Willingdon Light Buff Facings, delivered, was £189.20 per 1000 and this price had remained unchanged since before tender date. The rates for the *extra over* and *half brick walls* items were calculated as follows:

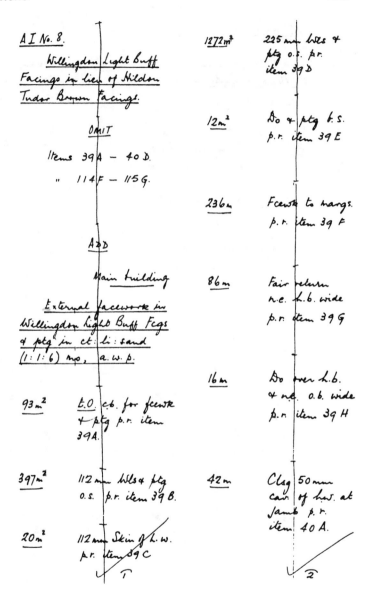

Shops & Flats, Thames St., Skinton

A I No. 8.

Willingdon Light Buff
Facings in lieu of Hildon
Tudor Brown Facings.

OMIT

Items 39A - 40 D.
  "   114F - 115 G.

ADD

Main building

External facework in
Willingdon Light Buff Fcgs
& ptg in ct : li : sand
(1 : 1 : 6) mo, a.w.p.

93 m²   E.O. c.b. for fcework
        & ptg p.r. item
        39A.

397 m² 112 mm hdls & ptg
        o.s. p.r. item 39 B.

20 m²   112 mm Skin of h.w.
        p.r. item 39 C

1272 m² 225 mm hdls &
         ptg o.s. p.r.
         item 39 D

12 m²   Do & ptg b.s.
         p.r. item 39 E

236 m   Fcework to margs.
         p.r. item 39 F

86 m   Fair return
         n.e. h.b. wide
         p.r. item 39 G

16 m   Do over h.b.
         & n.e. o.b. wide
         p.r. item 39 H

42 m   Clag 50 mm
         cav. of hw. at
         Jamb p.r.
         item 40 A.

Figure 12

Figure 12 (*cont.*)

Shops & Flats. Thames & Skinton

A.I. No. 8

Willingdon Light Buff Facings in lieu of
Hildon Tudor Brown Facings.

£   p

OMISSIONS

A   Items 39A - 40D inclusive   45226 04
B   "   114F - 115G   "   9981 96
    TOTAL OF OMISSIONS CARRIED TO SUMMARY   £ 55208 00

ADDITIONS

External facework in Willingdon
Light Buff Facings and pointing in
cement-lime mortar (1:1:6) as the
work proceeds.

C   Extra over common brickwork
    for facework p.r. item 39 A   93   m² 16.95   1576 35
D   112 mm Walls and pointing one
    side p.r. item 39B   397   m² 25.59 10159 23
E   112 mm Skins of hollow walls p.r.
    item 39 C   1272 m² 27.09 34458 48
F   225 mm Walls and pointing one
    side p.r. item 39 D   20   m² 42.51   850 20
G   225 mm Ditto and pointing both
    sides p.r. item 39 E   12   m² 49.90   598 80
H   Facework to margins p.r. item 39F   236   m   0.32   75 52
J   Fair return not exceeding
    half-brick wide p.r. item 39G   86   m   0.32   27 52
K   Ditto exceeding half-brick wide
    and not exceeding one brick wide
    p.r. item 39 H   16   m   2.87   45 92

                              carried forward   47792 02

Figure 12 (cont.)

Shops & Flats, Thames St., Swinton

AI No. 8 (cont.)

					£	p
	brought forward				47792	02
A	Closing 50 mm cavity of hollow walls at jambs p.r. item 40 A	42	m	3.05	128	10
B	Flush horizontal brick-on-end band, 225 mm wide in skins of hollow walls p.r. item 40 B	218	m	9.26	2018	68
C	Internal angle p.r. item 40 C	10	No.	1.15	11	50
D	External ditto p.r. item 40 D	14	No	1.15	16	10
E	Extra over common brickwork for facework p.r. item 114 F	18	m²	16.95	305	10
F	112 mm Walls and pointing both sides p.r. item 114 G	143	m²	32.98	4716	14
G	225 mm Ditto and pointing one side p.r. item 115 A	6	m²	42.51	255	06
H	225 mm Ditto and pointing both sides p.r. item 115 B	46	m²	49.90	2295	40
J	Facework to margins p.r. item 115 C	10	m	0.32	3	20
K	Fair return not exceeding half-brick side p.r. item 115 D	18	m	0.32	5	76
L	Ditto exceeding half-brick wide and not exceeding one brick wide p.r. item 115 E	11	m	2.87	31	57
M	Horizontal brick-on-end coping 225 mm high p.r item 115 F	182	m	9.62	1750	84
N	Angle p.r. item 115 G.	14	No	1.35	18	90

TOTAL OF ADDITIONS CARRIED TO SUMMARY   £ 59348 37

Figure 12 (*cont.*)

Extra over	£
Prime cost of Willingdon Light Buffs per 1000	189.20
Prime cost of Hildon Tudor Browns per 1000	176.50
Difference	12.70
81 bricks per m^2, Flemish Bond, @ £12.70 per 1000	1.03
15% OHP*	0.15
	1.18
Bill rate, item 39A	15.77
Required rate	16.95

Half brick walls	
61 bricks per m^2, Stretcher Bond, @ £12.70 per 1000	0.77
15% OHP	0.12
	0.89
Bill rate, item 39B	24.70
Required rate	25.59

AI No. 15 Roof slabs

This variation is shown using the format described on p. 102 in which the dimensions, billing and pricing are on the same sheet. The calculation of the *pro rata* rates for the additions was made as follows.

Concrete slab

The bill rate was first analysed to find the approximate rate used for the concrete at the mixer and this was then adjusted for the reduced labour input due to the increased thickness. It was considered that the increased size of reinforcing bars did not affect the placing of the concrete sufficiently to justify amendment of the labour content.

---

*The Contractor stated, upon request, that the tender included 15 per cent mark-up on nett cost for overheads and profit.

			£	p.
	A I No. 15.	Roof slab increased in thickness from 125 mm to 175 mm.		
		OMISSIONS		
A	53m³	125 mm Concrete flat roof slab as item 28 C	73.93 3918	29
B	293/ 12.00 = 3516.00 = 3094 kg	12 mm High tensile steel bar reinforcement in suspended roof as item 30 F	0.77 2382	38
C	110 m	Wrought formwork to edge of roof at eaves 295 mm girth as item 31 H.	6.06 666	60
		TOTAL OF OMISSIONS CARRIED TO SUMMARY £ 6967	27
		ADDITIONS		
D	74m³	175 mm Concrete flat roof slab p.r. item 28 C	71.93 5322	82
E	293/ 12.00 = 3516.00 = 5555 kg	16 mm High tensile steel bar reinforcement in suspended roof p.r item 30 F	0.63 3499	65
F	110 m	Wrought formwork to edge of roof at eaves, 345 mm girth p.r. item 31 H.	6.80 748	00
		TOTAL OF ADDITIONS CARRIED TO SUMMARY £ 9570	47

Shops & Flats, Thames St. Skinton

Figure 13

Analysis of the bill rate:

	£
Bill rate, item 28C	73.93
15% OHP (i.e. deduct $^{15}/_{115}$)	9.64
	64.29
Labour placing, say 9.00 man/hrs @ £4.12*	37.08
Cost of concrete at mixer per m^3	27.21

Build-up of new rate:

	£
Cost of concrete at mixer per m^3	27.21
Labour placing, say 8.50 man/hrs @ £4.12	35.02
	62.23
15% OHP	9.33
Required rate	71.56

Reinforcement

An increase in the diameter of reinforcing bars results in a lower cost per kilogramme of both the material and the labour content.

Analysis of the bill rate:

	£
Bill rate, item 30F, 12 mm bars, per kg	0.77
15% OHP	0.10
	0.67
Cost of bars	0.36
Labour, bending, and fixing	0.31

The balance of cost is reasonable for the required labour, thus indicating that the analysis of the bill rate is reasonable.

Build-up of new rate:

	£
16 mm high tensile steel bars, per kg	0.33
Labour bending and fixing, say	0.22
	0.55
15% OHP	0.08
Required rate	0.63

*All-in labour rate calculated in accordance with the principles of the IOB *Code of Estimating Practice*, including 30 per cent bonus.

Formwork

This rate was not worked out in detail. The increase in girth is about one-sixth and as the labour content would be rather less than proportionately increased, the bill rate of £6.06 was increased to £6.80.

AI No. 23 Larger windows in living rooms in flats

Only the items affected by the variation were omitted from the original dimensions, i.e. the 'vertical' items. It should be noted that the deduction of walling for the larger windows can be taken-off either as 'deducts' items in the additions, or as omissions items. In the former case, as in the example, the results show negative quantities and so these items have been billed as omission items with positive quantities.

The windows item in the bills was priced at a rate of £80.83. This was analysed and a rate found for the larger windows as follows:

	£
Bill rate, item 66E	80.83
15% OHP	10.54
	70.29
P.c. of window, delivered	63.08
Labour, handling and fixing	7.21

The labour for the larger window was increased by 20% and added to the p.c. of the larger window, as follows:

	£
P.c. window, delivered	75.24
Labour, handling and fixing	8.65
	83.89
15% OHP	12.58
Required rate	96.47

The remaining rates required to price the additions items are either bill rates or those used in pricing items in AI No. 8. The latter are the brick facework items for which rates are now contained in the additions items of AI No. 8. The original bill rates for those items are, of course, no longer relevant.

Shops & Flats, Thames St., Skinton

AI No. 23.   *Larger windows in Living Rooms.*

OMISSIONS.   £   P

A 18/ 1   18   Softwood windows size 1800×1200
                        mm. as D.J. Joinery Ltd's Catalogue   }80.83 1454 94
                        ref. WM1812N as item 64C

B 18/7/3/ 0.50
          0.35   18.90 4mm Clear float glass in panes
                        0.10 – 0.50 m² as item 100C   }21.65   449 50
   18/3/ 0.55
          0.37   10.99
                 ‾‾‾‾‾
                 29.89 = 30m²

C 18/ 1.80
       1.20   38.88 Prepare and paint two undercoats
                        and one gloss finishing coat on
                        ready primed wood windows   }3.87   150.93
                        internal as item 104A

                 = 39m²   &

D   Ditto external as item 105G   3.97   154.83

E 18/3/ 3.35   120.60 Ditto on edges of casements
                        external as item 105J   }0.44   53 24

                 = 121 m
                                              1500
                                              1200
                        add depth :   ‾‾‾‾
                                               300

F 18/ 1.80
       0.30   9.72   112 mm Skins of hollow walls in
                       facings as 'AI No.8, item 1E   }27.09   270 90

                 = 10m²   &

G   50 mm Cavity of hollow walls
                        as item 36 E   }0.86   8 60

                              &

H   100 mm Lightweight concrete block
                        Skins of hollow walls as   }11.44   114 40
                        item 37G
                                                          ‾‾‾‾‾‾‾
                        carried forward   2857 34

Figure 14

					£	p
				brought forward	2857	34

Shops or Flats, Thames St., Skinton

AI No 23 (cont)　OMISSIONS

A　18/ 1·80
　　　　0·30　9·72　Two-coat plaster on blockwork walls as item 93 D 〕 4·55　45　50

　　　　　= 10 m²　&

B　　　　　　Emulsion paint on plastered walls as item 103 A 〕 1·72　17　20

TOTAL OF OMISSIONS CARRIED TO SUMMARY £　2920　04

ADDITIONS

C　18/ 1　18　Softwood windows size 1800 x 1500 mm as D.T. Joinery Ltd's catalogue, ref. WM 1815 N p.r. item 64C 〕 96·47　1736　46

D　18/2/ 0·30　10·80　Bed frame and point one side as item 40 D 〕 0·79　8　69

　　　　= 11 m

E　18/4/ 0·55
　　　　　0·37　14·65　4 mm Clear float glass as item 100 C 〕 21·65　844　35
　18/2/4/ 0·50
　　　　　0·34　24·48
　　　　　　39·13　= 39 m²

F　18/ 1·80
　　　 1·50　48·60　Prepare and paint two undercoats and one gloss finishing coat on ready primed wood windows internal as item 104 A 〕 3·87　189　63

　　　　= 49 m²　&

G　　　　　　Ditto external as item 105 G　3·97　194　53

H　18/2/ 3·95　142·20　Ditto on edges of casements external as item 105 J 〕 0·44　62　48

　　　　= 142 m

　　　　　　　carried forward　3036　14

Figure 14 (*cont.*)

					£	p
				brought forward	3036	14

AI No. 23 (cont) ADDITIONS

Shops & Flats, Thames St, Skinton

A 18/2 0.30 10.80 Closing 50 mm cavity of hollow walls as item 36J] 1.47 16 17

= 11 m ⌇

B Vertical dampproof course 112 mm wide as item 38C] 0.86 9 46

⌇

C Fair return not exceeding half-brick wide as AI No 8, item 17] 0.32 3 52

⌇

D Two-coat plaster on blockwork walls not exceeding 300 mm wide as item 93F

Sq × 0.16 = 1.73 m² = 2 m² 5.45 10 90

⌇

E Emulsion paint on plastered walls as item 103A = 2 m² 1.72 3 44

⌇

F External angle as item 93J 0.79 8 69

= 11 m

TOTAL OF ADDITIONS CARRIED TO SUMMARY £ 3088 32

Figure 14 (*cont.*)

AI No. 28 Glazing to balcony screens

In order to determine a rate for the obscure glazing, the bill rate was analysed and a new rate was then synthesized from the resulting data, thus:

	£
Bill rate, item 99G, per m²	23.21
15% OHP	3.48
	19.73
4 mm float glass, including waste	17.82
Labour	1.91

The balance left for labour is reasonable, representing 0.40 man/hrs, (on the basis of an 'all-in' craftsman's rate of £4.81 per hour). So again, the data from the analysis may be used for building-up a new rate, as follows:

	£
4 mm obscure glass, group 2	14.74
Putty and glazing sprigs, say,	0.38
Labour as before + 20%	2.32
	17.44
15% OHP	2.62
Required rate	20.06

The difference in the rate for the glazing in panes 0.50–1.00 m² will be proportionate to the difference between the respective clear glass rates, i.e. £18.59.

AI No. 41 New door to existing store

The omissions relate to the redecoration of the existing window, as provided for in the bills.

The contractor submitted Daywork Sheet No. 6, dated 27 March 1988 showing all the labour and materials expended. The PQS decided, however, that the new joinery, ironmongery and painting were items that were properly measurable and priceable and should not therefore be valued as dayworks. The carpenter's, painter's, and part of the labourer's time as well as the relevant materials, have therefore been omitted from the daywork account.

The labour rates and materials prices used in valuing the daywork are those current at the dates when the work was done, i.e. 24–25 March 1988. The labour rates have been calculated in accordance with Section 3 of the *Definition of Prime Cost of Dayworks carried out under a Building Contract*. The respective percentage additions are those tendered by the contractor in the bills (see Appendix A, p. 227).

An addition item for which there was no directly comparable bill item was the fixing item for the push plate. A rate was used which was equivalent to that used for other surface-fixed items of ironmongery – e.g. numerals, hat-and-coat hooks – priced at £0.96.

Shops & Flats, Thames St., Skinton

	A I No. 28	Glazing to balcony screens.			
		OMISSIONS		£	p
A	18/2/ 0·55 0·63	10·49	4mm Clear float glass and glazing to wood with beads and glazing strip in panes 0·10 – 0·56 m² as item 99G	23·21	324	94
	18/ 0·47 0·45	3·81			
		14·30 = 14 m²			
B	18/2/ 0·55 1·17	23·17	4mm Ditto in panes 0·50–1·00 m² as item 99F	21·51	688	32
	18/ 0·47 1·08	9·14			
		32·31 = 32 m²			
C	18/2/ 2·16 18/ 1·84 18/2/ 3·44	77·76 33·12 123·84	10 x 30 mm Mahogany glazing beads as item 65J	1·80	523	80
			&		
D	18/ 3·10	55·80 290·52	Glazing strip as item 100D	0·65	189	15
		= 291 m.			

TOTAL OMISSIONS CARRIED TO SUMMARY £ 1726 21

ADDITIONS.

E	14 m²	4mm Pattern group 2 obscure glass and glazing to wood with glazing compound in panes 0·10 – 0·50 m² p.r. item 99G	20·06	280	84
F	32 m²	4mm Ditto in panes 0·50–1·00 m² as item 99F.	18·59	594	88

TOTAL ADDITIONS CARRIED TO SUMMARY £ 875 72

Figure 15

The door item was priced *pro rata* to item 58C, which was for a similar type of door but size 762 × 1981 mm. The rate was arrived at as follows:

	£	£
Bill rate, item 57C		32.60
Additional prime cost of 838 mm door	0.98	
Additional labour allowance	0.60	
	1.58	
15% OHP	0.24	1.82
Required rate		34.42

The door frame item was priced *pro rata* to bill item 57D which was for a door frame size 762 × 1981 mm, taking into account also other items for frames. The items in the bills were

	£
50 × 88 mm Frame for door size 762 × 1981 mm	20.54
50 × 88 mm Frame for door size 838 × 1981 mm	21.12
63 × 88 mm Frame for door size 762 × 1981 mm	25.12

On a size proportion basis, the rate was determined at £25.82. The remaining items were priced at bill rates.

AI No. 48 Omission of bookcase units

The omissions formed a complete section of the original taking-off and cols. 325–336 of the dimensions were marked 'X' at the beginning and end of the section for ease of reference. The items involved formed a separate group in the Joinery section of the bills and were omitted in the variation accounts as a group together with the related decoration items.

The consequential additions items were all deduction items in the original dimensions, and, upon identification for omissions purposes, they were converted into additions items with positive quantities (*see* comments under AI No. 23, p. 120).

<u>A I No. 41</u> <u>New door to existing Store.</u>

OMISSIONS. £ p

A 0.63
  <u>0.90</u> 0.57 Prepare and paint one undercoat ⎤
                    and one gloss finishing coat ⎟
                    on existing wood window   ⎟
                    internal as item 104 K   ⎦ 3.10 3 10

              = 1 m²   4

B   Ditto external as item 106 M 3.20 3 20

C 2.67   Ditto on edges of casement as ⎤ 0.35 1 05
             item 106 P   ⎦

             = 3 m

             TOTAL OMISSIONS CARRIED TO SUMMARY £   7 35

             ADDITIONS

D   1   44 mm Exterior quality ply-faced ⎤
             door, size 838 x 1981 mm, p.r.   ⎟ 34.42 34 42
             item 58 C   ⎦

                    4

E   63 x 89 mm Door frame, rebated, ⎤
             for door, size 838 x 1981 mm, p.r.⎟ 25.82 25 82
             item 57 D   ⎦

F 2/ 3   6 Frame tie as item 73 L 0.64 3 84
                              7/1981 838
                                     2962
                              7/750 4800
                                      200
                                     5000.

G 5.00   Bedding frame and pointing one ⎤ 0.79 3 95
             side as item 40 D.   ⎦

             = 5 m

H 1½   Pair 100 mm steel butts as item 68 D 3.58 5 37

                    carried forward   73 40

Figure 16

Shops — Flats, Thames St., Steinton

	AI No. 41 (cont)	ADDITIONS		£	p
		brought forward		73	40
A	1	Fixing mortice deadlock as item 68M 5.82		5	82
		&			
B		Ditto 75 × 200 mm pull handle 1.20		1	20
		&			
C		Ditto 75 × 200 mm push plate 0.96		0	96
		&			
D		Ditto door closer as item 68Q 4.80		4	80
E	0.88 2.03 1.79	Knot, prime, stop and paint two undercoats and one gloss finishing coat on wood surfaces internal as item 104D 3.87 = 2 m² &		7	74
F		Ditto external as item 105K 3.97		7	94
G	4.90	Ditto on wood frame not exceeding 150 mm girth internal as item 104G 1.07 = 5m &		5	35
H		Ditto external as item 106B 1.12		5	60
J		Daywork account as daywork sheet no 6 dated 27/3/88 :—			
		Labour 141.80 50% addition 70.90		212	70
		Materials 37.39 20% addition 7.48		44	87
		TOTAL ADDITIONS CARRIED TO SUMMARY £		370	38

Figure 16 *(cont.)*

BEECON Ltd. River Rd, Skinton

Contract <u>Shops and Flats, Thames St, Skinton</u>

Work commenced <u>24 March 1988</u>

Work completed <u>25 March 1988</u>

Daywork sheet No. <u>6</u>   Date <u>27 March 1988</u>

AI No. <u>41</u>   Take out window from existing Store. Alter opening as necessary to form door opening and provide and build in Catnic lintel. Provide and fix 838 x 1981 mm door and frame, fix deadlock, handles and closer (provided out of p.c. sum for ironmongery).

Labour	Hrs.	Rate	£	p
Bricklayer	20	3.86	76	20
Carpenter	8		-	-
Labourer	20/24	3.28	65	60
Painter	6		-	-
			141	80
Plant				

Materials	Qty	Rate	£	p
Facing bricks	60 No	105.16	6	31
450 x 225 x 100 mm Thermalite blocks	18 No	53p	9	54
Mortar	1 m³	31.26	1	56
Catnic steel cavity lintel, 1500 mm	1 No	17.93	17	93
112 mm dampcourse	5 m	41p	2	05
838 x 1981 mm External quality ply-faced flush door	1 No	msd	-	-
Door frame set	1 No			
Undercoat paint	1 lt			
Gloss paint	1 lt			
			37	39

Site agent's signature *W. Jones.*

The information shown on this sheet has been verified (except rates and prices)
Architect's/Architect's representative's signature *A. Brown*

Figure 17

Figure 18

AI No. 48
Omission of bookcase units.

		OMISSIONS			£	p
A		Items 66A to 66K inclusive			3559	68
B		Item 68C			241	92
C		Item 68F			18	36
D		Prepare and two coats poly-urethane clear finish on wood general surfaces as item 107A	40	m²	1.57	62	80
E		Ditto 150-300 mm girth as item 107B	119	m	0.48	57	12

TOTAL OMISSIONS CARRIED TO SUMMARY £3939 88

ADDITIONS

F		25 x 100 mm Softwood skirtings as item 65C	38	m	1.51	57	38
G		Emulsion paint on plastered walls as item 103A	87	m²	1.72	149	64
H		Prime only wood skirtings before fixing not exceeding 150mm girth internal as item 103L	38	m	0.21	7	98
J		Knot, prime, stop and paint two undercoats and one gloss finishing coat on ditto not exceeding 150 mm girth internal as item 104F.	38	m	1.12	42	56

TOTAL ADDITIONS CARRIED TO SUMMARY £257 56

Figure 18 (*cont.*)

REFERENCES

1. *Standard Method of Measurement of Building Works, Seventh Edition* (London: RICS 1988) p. 11.
2. *Definition of Prime Cost of Daywork carried out under a Building Contract* (London: RICS 1975).
3. RICS, Questions and Answers, *Chartered Quantity Surveyor*, Vol. 8, No. 8, 1986, p. 8.
4. SIMS, J. Contracts, *Building*, 1975, Vol. 228, No. 6, p. 83; and Vol. 229, No. 49, p. 72.
5. JCT, *Consolidated Main Contract Formula Rules* (London: RIBA Publications Ltd, 1987).
6. BCIS, *Guide to Daywork Rates* (Kingston-upon-Thames: RICS, 1988).
7. KEATING, D., *Law and Practice of Building Contracts* (London: Sweet & Maxwell, 1978), p. 315; WALKER-SMITH, *The Standard Forms of Building Contract* (London: Charles Knight & Co. Ltd, 1971), p. 43.

9

Fluctuations – traditional method of reimbursement

INTRODUCTION

Any contract, other than a prime cost contract, will be either 'firm price' or 'fluctuating price'. *Firm price contracts* are those where reimbursement of changes in costs is limited to those relating to statutory contributions, levies, and taxes. *Fluctuating price contracts* are those containing provisions for reimbursement of changes in a wide range of labour costs and materials prices in addition to statutory costs. It should be recognized that the term 'fluctuations' includes both increases and decreases and that they may lead to payments becoming due to the contractor from the Employer and vice versa.

The JCT Form contains three different provisions, any one of which may be incorporated in a contract by deleting the other two clause references in the Appendix to the Conditions of the Contract. These provisions are:

(*a*) adjustment of the contract sum limited to fluctuations in statutory contributions, levies and taxes, as specified in clause 38.

(*b*) adjustment of the contract sum in respect of fluctuations in labour and materials costs and in statutory contributions, levies and taxes, as specified in clause 39.

(*c*) adjustment of the contract sum in respect of fluctuations as in (*b*) above by the NEDO Formula method, as specified in clause 40.

(*a*) and (*b*) above relate to what may be called the *traditional method* of reimbursement of the actual amount of fluctuations allowed under the respective clauses of the contract, and (*c*) to the *formula method* of calculating by use of formulae a sum to compensate for loss due to fluctuations. This method is discussed in Chapter 10.

TRADITIONAL METHOD

The object of the traditional method is to ascertain the actual amount of the fluctuations in costs and prices within the scope of the appropriate clauses of the contract, as given above. That amount will often be less, sometimes much less, than the total amount by which costs and prices have really fluctuated, due to the limitations imposed by the operation of the contract clauses. Those costs and prices may be considered under the three main headings referred to in the JCT Form.

Statutory contributions, levies, and taxes relative to 'workpeople' and others

Clauses 38 and 39.2 are similar and provide for the reimbursement of fluctuations occurring after the Base Date in (i) the amounts of any statutory contribution, levy or tax which, at the Base Date, the contractor is liable to pay or (ii) the amount of any refund of any such contribution, levy or tax which is receivable by the contractor at the Base Date, as an employer of workpeople (as defined in clauses 38 and 39). The Base Date is defined as 'the date stated in the Appendix to the Conditions'.

Examples of these costs are: employers' National Health Insurance contributions and contributions under the Social Security Pensions Act 1975. The wording of the clauses provides not only for changes in contributions, etc., operative at the Base Date but also for new types of contribution or tax which may be imposed and for existing ones which may be abolished.

The provisions of clause 38 relate not only to operatives employed on site but also to:

(*a*) persons who are directly employed elsewhere by the contractor in the production of materials or goods for the Works, such as joinery shop workers; and

(*b*) persons, such as timekeepers and site surveyors, who, although employed by the contractor on site, are not 'workpeople' as defined in the clause. Amounts in respect of this class of persons are the same as for a craftsman, but in proportion to the amount of time spent on site per week, within certain specified limitations.

Labour costs in addition to statutory costs

Clause 39.1 deals with fluctuations in labour costs other than those imposed by statute. In this sub-clause, the basis of the prices in the bills or schedule of rates is first defined and then it is provided that any increases or decreases within the prescribed limits shall be paid to or allowed by the contractor.

The basis of adjustment is 'the rules or decisions of the National Joint Council for the Building Industry' and these are embodied in the *National Working Rule Agreement*. This agreement sets out basic wage rates, extra payments to which operatives may be entitled and various matters relating to working conditions. It also includes the provisions of the Annual Holidays Agreement and the amounts of weekly holiday credits for each operative for which an employer is liable. Specific reference is made in clause 39.1 to employers' liability insurance and third party insurance, which brings the respective premiums within the reimbursement provisions, for the reason that the premiums are usually calculated as a percentage of a contractor's wages bill.

It should be noted that the rates of wages referred to are those 'in accordance with the rules or decisions of the National Joint Council'. Where operatives are paid at higher wage rates than the nationally-negotiated rates, the basis of the prices in the contract bills or schedule of rates is no longer as stated in clause 39.1.1 and therefore clause 39.1.2 cannot follow.[1]

Operatives employed by 'domestic' (non-nominated) sub-contractors (whether on a labour-only basis or not) rank for recovery of fluctuations in the same way as, and on a similar basis to, the main contractor's directly employed labour,[2] provided that the contractor has complied with the requirement of clause 39.4.1.

The classes of persons coming within the scope of clause 39 are the same as those to which clause 38 applies, as described above.

Materials costs

Where clause 39 applies

The basis of adjustment is a list of materials (and goods) with their basic prices. Both materials and prices may be entered by the contractor on a blank form attached to the bills (see Appendix A, p. 230) at the same time as they are priced or the form may be required to be filled in and returned with the Form of Tender. Sometimes, the principal materials may be listed on the form by the PQS, the contractor adding the prices when tendering. The prices on the list are intended to be market prices current at the Base Date and once the contract is signed, they must be regarded as such anyway. Any fluctuations, to be allowable for recovery, must first, relate to materials named on the list and secondly, be due solely to changes in the market prices. Such changes may arise from or include, a change in tax or duty on a material or from either the abolition of existing duty or tax or the imposition of new types of duty or tax.

Sometimes, claims are made in respect of changes in price which are due to other causes than changes in market prices. These may be: buying in part loads or small quantities, obtaining materials from another supplier at less favourable discounts, or because the material is not the same as, although similar to, that on the Basic Prices List. Adjustments to the contract sum should not be made for fluctuations in prices due to these or similar causes.

Clause 39.7.2 is specific that timber used in formwork ranks for fluctuations recovery (provided timber is on the Basic Prices List) although it is not part of the permanent work. Other consumable stores, plant and machinery do not, with the exception of electricity and, where specifically stated on the Basic Prices List, fuels.

The inclusion in a claim of materials drawn from the contractor's stores sometimes presents a problem, if the contractor is unable to produce invoices for them. Clause 39.3.2 is specific that the sum to be paid to or allowed by the contractor is to be the difference between the prices on the Basic Prices List and the market prices current when the materials were bought, and which were payable by the contractor. Some PQSs will not include materials from stock for which the contractor cannot produce an invoice. Others will include them on assumed purchase prices equivalent to those being paid for other quantities of the same materials.

Materials used by 'domestic' (non-nominated) sub-contractors rank equally with those used directly by the general contractor and on the same basis, provided that the contractor has complied with the requirement of clause 39.4.1.

The PQS should check the total quantities of each material listed in the claim to see that they are not in excess of those reasonably required, remembering to make allowances for reasonable losses due to wastage and theft. Any excess quantities should, of course, be excluded.

Where clause 38 applies

The basis of adjustment is a list (but no prices) attached to the contract bills, of materials, goods, electricity and, where specifically stated in the contract documents, fuels. Any adjustments allowable are limited to changes in types or rates of duty or tax relative to any of the materials or goods, etc., listed, and to price changes due to the abolition of a type of duty or tax or to the imposition of a new one. The comments made in the preceding section apply here also.

NOMINATED SUB-CONTRACTORS AND NOMINATED SUPPLIERS

Claims for fluctuations from nominated sub-contractors and nominated suppliers are specifically excluded from the provisions of clauses 38 and 39, being dealt with under the provisions of the respective sub-contracts and contracts of sale. If the sub-contracts and contracts of sale contain clauses which provide for the recovery of fluctuations, then the amounts properly recoverable under them will be payable to or allowable by the general contractor, as the case may be.

With regard to nominated sub-contracts, where the Standard Form of Nominated Sub-contract is used (NSC/4 or NSC/4a), clauses 35 to 37 inclusive are parallel to clauses 38 to 40 of the main contract. Any proper claims for reimbursement of fluctuations under the appropriate sub-contract clauses will then form part of the amounts payable to the general contractor by the Employer under clause 30.6.2.6 of the main contract. The PQS will need to know, therefore, in order to check a sub-contractor's account, what the details are in Schedule 1 of the Standard Form of Nominated Sub-Contract Tender NSC/1 attached to the sub-contract.

With regard to contracts of sale between the contractor and nominated suppliers, the provisions of each contract will determine what fluctuations (if any) are properly recoverable. Those that are, as in the case of sub-contracts, will become part of the amounts 'properly chargeable to the Employer' under clause 30.6.2.8.

ADDITIONS TO NETT SUMS RECOVERABLE

The sums calculated for fluctuations are not subject to any profit addition (*see* clauses 38.4.6 and 39.5.6 of the JCT Form) but an addition should be made of the percentage stated in the Appendix to the Conditions as provided in clauses 38.7 and 39.8. This addition applies to all fluctuation amounts recoverable under the provisions of clauses 38 and 39.

The percentage addition was introduced in order to go some way towards meeting the objections of contractors that only a small proportion of the true amounts of the increased costs actually incurred was being recovered.

EXCLUSIONS

The following kinds of work are excluded from the fluctuations provisions of clauses 38 and 39 of the JCT Form.

(*a*) Work paid for on a daywork basis. This is because the rates used for valuing daywork should be rates current at the time the work is done. Those rates are used (and not tender date rates) because of the percentage additions made to the prime costs (see p. 107).

(*b*) Work carried out by a nominated sub-contractor and materials and goods supplied by a nominated supplier. As stated above, fluctuations relative to work or materials in this category are dealt with under clauses 35 and 36.

(*c*) Work carried out by the contractor which is the subject of a prime cost sum and for which the contractor submitted a tender under clause 35.2. The reason here is the same as in (*b*) above.

(*d*) Changes in value added tax charged by the contractor to the Employer.

RECORDING AND CHECKING FLUCTUATIONS CLAIMS

It is in the interests of the contractor and the PQS that a satisfactory system of recording and submitting the details of fluctuations claims be agreed at the start of the contract. This means that the system employed should facilitate the checking of the details from original invoices, wages sheets, etc. The amount of checking required can be considerable and the more systematic the contractor is in recording the data and preparing his claim, the sooner the checking and computation of the sums payable can be completed.

In order that amounts due may be paid without delay, the contractor should present claims at regular intervals, say, weekly or fortnightly. All supporting documents should be provided for the PQS's inspection when checking the claim and it is useful to have the signature of the clerk of works, if there is one, on time sheets to certify the correctness of the names and hours shown. Alternatively, if a standard claim form is used to record the data taken from time sheets, provision may be made on the form for certification of the correctness of that data.

Figure 19 shows a summary of part of the materials claim relating to the contract of which particulars are given in Appendix A. The claim was prepared in accordance with the particulars shown in the Appendix to the Conditions of the contract, i.e. under the provisions of clause 39. Only the increases in the cost of cement are shown, being part only of the complete materials fluctuations claim. The higher price of the May delivery was due to the small quantity and not to an increase in market price. It was therefore reduced by the PQS to the rate appropriate to full loads.

PAYMENT

Payment of amounts recoverable is required to be made in the next interim certificate after ascertaining, from time to time, the amounts due. Such amounts are not subject to retention. The total amount of fluctuations will also be included in the final account as an addition or deduction, as the case may be.

FLUCTUATIONS AFTER EXPIRY OF THE CONTRACT PERIOD

A frequent cause for dispute in the past was whether the contractor was entitled to be paid for increases in costs relative to the period between the 'Date for Completion' (i.e. the date, as stated in the Appendix or extended, by which the Contract should have been completed) and the date of actual completion. It is now

BEECON Ltd. River Rd, Skinton

Contract Shops and Flats, Thames St, Skinton

Material Ordinary Portland Cement   **Materials fluctuations claim**

Basic price £51.04   Sheet No. 1

Supplier	Invoice No. and date	Quantity	Invoice price	Decrease £	Decrease p	Increase £	Increase p	Total decrease £	Total decrease p	Total increase £	Total increase p
Grey Square Cement Co. Ltd	DF897 16.11.07	20 tonnes	52.95			1	91			38	20
" " "	LK1376 11.1.80	10 "	52.95			1	91			19	10
Greenthorne Cement Co. Ltd	GZ736X 15.3.80	12 "	52.95			1	91			22	92
" " "	K1556Z 5.4.80	10 "	52.95			1	91			19	10
" " "	K2485W 2.5.80	2 "	52.95 / 56.53			1	91			2	82
Grey Square Cement Co. Ltd	PR884 10.7.80	6 "	52.95			1	91			11	46
" " "	DL1285 20.9.80	6 "	55.60			4	56			27	36

Nett total carried to summary £   141 96

Figure 19

clearly established that fluctuations amounts are recoverable until the date of actual completion, that is, including the period after the date by which the contract should have been completed. The decision of the Court of Appeal in the case of *Peak Construction (Liverpool) Limited v. McKinney Foundations Limited (1970), 69 LGR 1*, settled the matter and although the contract in that case was not based on the JCT Form, the Joint Contracts Tribunal has accepted the judgment as applying to the JCT Form.[3]

The JCT Form, in clauses 38.4.7 and 39.5.7, 'freezes' the amount of fluctuations, however, at the levels which are operative at the Completion Date (as stated in the contract or as extended). Consequently, although fluctuations should be calculated up to the date of actual completion, such calculations should be made on the basis of the changes in costs and prices occurring up to, but not after, the Completion Date.

OTHER NON-RECOVERABLE FLUCTUATIONS

It has already been pointed out (*see* p. 135) that where a contractor pays operatives at rates above the nationally-negotiated rates, the provisions of clause 39 no longer apply. That clause applies only to 'rules of wages and other emoluments and expenses . . . payable . . . in accordance with the rules or decisions of the National Joint Council for the Building Industry . . .'. Any fluctuations in such inflated rates of wages are not recoverable, even where the fluctuations are related to nationally-agreed rates.

The non-productive hours of overtime (even when expressly authorized) should not be included in allowable fluctuations payments. Only the actual hours worked rank for reimbursement.

Also excluded is the time spent on making good defects under the provisions of clause 17. Such work is required to be done entirely at the contractor's expense.

REFERENCES

1. The Query Sheet, *Chartered Surveyor, BQS Quarterly*, Vol. 2, No. 4, Summer 1975, p. 56.
2. Questions and Answers, *Chartered Surveyor, BQS Quarterly*, Vol. 4, No. 1, Autumn 1976, p. 15.
3. The Query Sheet, *Chartered Surveyor, BQS Quarterly*, Vol. 2, No. 2, Winter 1974, p. 27.

10

Fluctuations – formula method of reimbursement

In contrast to the traditional method of reimbursement of fluctuations, the object of the formula method is to calculate a sum or sums which will compensate the parties to the contract for loss incurred due to increases and decreases in costs. No attempt is made to calculate the *actual* amount of loss involved. Consequently, the sums recoverable by the formula method will differ from those recoverable under the traditional method and will usually be greater.[1]

The formula method is incorporated in the 'with quantities', 'without quantities' and 'with approximate quantities' variants of the JCT Form, in both Local Authorities and Private Editions, by means of clause 40 as the alternative to clauses 38 and 39. It may also be used for schedule of rates contracts.

The JCT Form refers in clause 40.1 to a separate document called the *Formula Rules*[2] which sets out the formulae and defines their use. By virtue of the provisions of clause 40, the *Formula Rules* are made part of the Standard Form and, therefore, contractually binding on the parties.[3]

The application of the formulae is by means of indices, published monthly by the Property Services Agency of the Department of the Environment, which measure the fluctuations in costs of building work classified in forty-nine categories.* The indices are intended to be applied monthly to the sums included in interim valuations, thus ensuring that the payment of fluctuations is

---

*Work Groups may be used instead. A Work Group is 'a work category or combination of work categories as defined in the contract bills'. Wherever the term 'work category' is used hereafter, the words 'or work group' are to be implied where appropriate.

made promptly. The index number for each work category is based upon price movements of a number of selected items of labour, materials and plant which are calculated from a range of contracts.

It follows, therefore that the sums produced by the application of the indices to the prices in interim valuations must necessarily reflect a *general* fluctuation in prices and cannot relate to *actual* fluctuations in labour, materials and plant costs applicable to a particular contract.

PREPARATORY WORK NECESSARY BEFORE USING THE FORMULAE

The *Formula Rules* give a formula for application to each work category (Rule 9), a second one relative to *balance of adjustable work* (i.e. work ranking for adjustment but which is not capable of allocation to any work category) (Rule 26), and a third formula for use for valuations after Practical Completion and in the Final Certificate (Rule 28). After giving corresponding formulae for use with work groups (Rules 29 and 38), five formulae applicable to five types of specialist engineering installations are given (Rules 50, 54, 58, 63 and 69).

In order to apply the appropriate formula to each work category, all the measured work items in the bills of quantities must be allocated to work categories. This should be done before tenders are invited, either by annotating the bills or by preparing schedules. Then, when interim valuations are done, the value of work included in them must be allocated accordingly. Annotating bills may be done by giving the work category number against each item in a column next to the item reference column.

There will be some work or goods the value of which is included in a valuation, which cannot easily (if at all) be allocated to work categories or which is excluded from adjustment and these are dealt with as discussed below.

Balance of adjustable work

This is the balance of main contractor's work which ranks for adjustment but which is not allocated to work categories or to which an engineering formula does not apply. Examples are preliminaries, water for the works, insurances, attendances on nominated sub-contractors. The amount of the adjustment to the balance of adjustable work for any valuation period is in the same proportion as the total amount of adjustment of work allocated to work categories bears to the total value of work in all work categories.

Multiple category items

Sometimes a bill item, such as an alterations item in a 'Works on Site' bill, may relate to work falling within more than one work category. Such an item is allocated to the work category to which the largest part of the item relates.

Provisional sums

Provisional sums for work which will be paid at current prices (e.g. dayworks, work carried out by statutory undertakers and other public bodies), are not allocated to work categories but are separately identified as not subject to adjustment.

Provisional sums for work to be carried out by the general contractor are not allocated to work categories in the bills, but when the work has been executed, the measured items set against the provisional sum will then be allocated to appropriate categories or, if relating to specialist work, will be adjusted using the appropriate formula.

Fixing of items supplied either by nominated suppliers or by the Employer

'Fix only' items may be dealt with either by (a) allocating to an appropriate work category; (b) including in the balance of adjustable work; or (c) by applying an index specially created for the purpose. Whichever method is used must have been previously specified in the bills or agreed with the contractor in writing.

Variations

All additions items priced at bill rates or analogous rates or at rates current at the Base Date will rank for adjustment and should be allocated to work categories. Variations valued on a daywork basis or otherwise valued at rates or prices current at the date of execution should be excluded from the operation of the formulae.

Payments to nominated sub-contractors and nominated suppliers

Such payments, including profit, are excluded from the adjustment. Amounts for attendances on nominated sub-contractors are included in the balance of adjustable work (*see* 'Balance of adjustable work' above).

Unfixed materials and goods

The value of unfixed materials and goods is excluded from adjustment. Only when they have been incorporated into the work will they become adjustable in one of the ways described above.

Claims for loss and/or expense

Claims for extra payments under clauses 26 and 34.3 are similarly excluded as they will be valued at their full value.

CALCULATION OF ADJUSTMENT AMOUNTS

The appropriate formula is applied to each part of the value of work included in a valuation (after deducting the value of any work not subject to adjustment) when it has been apportioned into (*a*) work categories, (*b*) balance of adjustable work, and (*c*) specialist engineering installations. Such application is subject to the following considerations.

Provisional indices

Indices for any month when first published are provisional. Normally, firm indices are published three months later. The calculation of the adjustment amounts initially will also be provisional and will be subject to revision when the next valuation is done following publication of the firm indices.

Base month

The base month from which adjustment is calculated is the calendar month stated in the Appendix to the Conditions, which normally is the one prior to that in which the tender is due for return. The published index numbers for the base month will be used in the application of the formulae.

Valuation period

The value of work carried out during the valuation period is substituted in the formula and this period is defined as commencing on the day after that on which the immediately preceding valuation was done and finishing on the date of the succeeding valuation.

The index numbers for the valuation period are those for the month in which the mid-point of the valuation period occurs. If the valuation period has an odd number of days, then it will be the middle day of the period; if it contains an even number of days, the mid-point will be the middle day of the period remaining after deducting the last day.

Non-adjustable element

The non-adjustable element deduction applies only to contracts based on the local authorities edition of the JCT 'with quantities' Form.

RETENTION

The fluctuations amounts calculated by the formula method, unlike those ascertained by the traditional method, are subject to retention deductions. The reason for this is that what the formula method really does is to effect an updating of the rates and prices in the contract bills. The original rates and prices when included in valuations are subject to retention and it is logical, therefore, that the updated ones should be also.

APPLICATION OF THE FORMULA RULES TO WORK EXECUTED AFTER THE COMPLETION DATE (OR EXTENDED COMPLETION DATE)

Under the provisions of clause 40.7 of the JCT Form. the formula is applied to the value of work executed after the completion date (or extended completion date) but using the index numbers applicable to the month in which that date falls. This has the same effect as if all the work remaining to be done after the completion date had been carried out during the month in which the completion date occurred. It should be noted that this provision will not apply if either clause 25 has been amended or the architect has failed to fix or confirm the completion date in accordance with the provisions of clause 25.

ADJUSTMENT OF VALUE OF WORK INCLUDED IN INTERIM VALUATIONS ISSUED AFTER THE ISSUE OF THE CERTIFICATE OF PRACTICAL COMPLETION

Rule 28 of the *Formula Rules* gives the formula to be used for adjusting the value of executed work which is included in interim certificates issued after the Certificate of Practical Completion has been issued, such value, in consequence, not being attributable to any valuation period. The formula effects an adjustment to such value in the same proportion as the total fluctuations included in previous certificates bears to the total value of work included in such certificates. Put another way, the adjustment is calculated on the basis of the average fluctuations over the contract period.

This provision would apply to the difference between the actual value and an approximate valuation of variations and/or remeasured work and to the difference between the balance of adjustable work contained in the final account (and therefore in the Final Certificate) and that in respect of which fluctuations have already been included in interim certificates.

ERRORS

'Mechanical' errors

Possible errors, which may arise in the course of using the formula method, are listed in Rule 5a of the *Formula Rules*. They are:

(*a*) arithmetical errors in the calculation of the adjustment;

(*b*) incorrect allocation of value to work categories or to work groups;

(*c*) incorrect allocation of work as Contractor's Specialist Work;

(*d*) use of an incorrect index number or index numbers.

If any such error has occurred, then the PQS is required to correct it. Rule 5c requires that, when making the correction, the same index numbers are used as were used when the original calculation was done, except that firm index numbers, if available, should be substituted for provisional ones.

Rule 5b provides for the contractor to be granted access, if he so requests, to the 'working documents' which show the calculations of the fluctuations included in an interim certificate for payment, so that he may satisfy himself that errors of the kind referred to above have not been made.

Errors in preparing a valuation

The *Formula Rules* make no provision for the retrospective correction of errors made in the course of preparing an interim valuation. Such 'errors' include the valuation of provisional items of work at the quantities given in the bills which upon remeasurement are found to be different.

The *NEDO Guide* advises that 'valuations should be as firm and accurate as possible as these will not normally be reassessed at a later date'.[4] The Quantity Surveyors (Practice and Management) Committee of the RICS has stated the view that, if errors have occurred in the preparation of a valuation, they should be corrected but that, once firm index numbers have been substituted for provisional ones, the facility for such correction will no longer exist.[5]

When errors of this kind are corrected in the manner envisaged by the RICS Quantity Surveyors Committee, the correction will be effected in the same way as described for 'mechanical' errors, that is, as set out in Rule 5c.

Any further corrections which may remain to be made after firm index numbers have been applied, however, may be dealt with in the same way as the value of work included in interim certificates issued after Practical Completion (*see* above). In other words, adjustment of the errors may be made on the basis of the average of fluctuations over the whole of the contract period.

EXAMPLES

The following examples relate to the contract of which particulars are given in Appendix A. The application of the Formula Method, using work categories, is shown as it would have applied had the fluctuations provision been based on clause 40. The Base Month would then have been stated on the Appendix to the Conditions as January 1987. For the purposes of the example, Valuation No. 12 in the examples given at the end of Chapter 12 has been used.

It was necessary, prior to Valuation No. 1, to make preparatory calculations as follows:

(*a*) to ascertain from the bills the value of work in each of the appropriate work categories and this was done on Form A[6] (exclusions are: preliminaries, prime cost and provisional sums, including general contractor's profit and attendances on nominated sub-contractors, builder's work in connection with plumbing and builder's work in connection with electrical installation);

(*b*) to calculate the balance of adjustable work, as shown on Form B[7];

(*c*) to enter on Form WC1/WC2* the published Base Month index numbers for all the work categories involved.

The foregoing information was then available for use when each valuation was done.

When Valuation No. 12 was carried out on 25 March 1988, the following procedure was followed:

(*a*) the value of the work done *since the last valuation* which could be allocated to work categories, was entered in column 3 on Form WC1/WC2 (*see* p. 155). In column 4, under the heading 'Provisional', the index numbers for March for the relevant categories were entered. In column 5 were entered the adjusted valuation amounts using the expression.

$$V \times \frac{I_v}{I_o} \text{ where}$$

V = value of work executed in the work category during the valuation period;

*Forms WC1 and WC2 have been combined in the examples.

I_v = index number for the work category for the month during which the mid-point of the valuation period occurred;

I_o = the work category index number for the Base Month.[8]

The Price Adjustment Indices for March (provisional) and for December (firm) are reproduced in Figure 20 (from *Building*, 25.3.88, p. 14).

PRICE ADJUSTMENT INDICES

Index No	Dec"	Mar*	Building works (Series 2)
1	283	284	Demolitions and alterations
2	279	280	Site preparation, excavation and disposal
3	300	301	Hardcore and imported filling
4	288	289	General piling
5	240	240	Sheet steel piling
6	278	280	Concrete
7	244	247	Reinforcement
8	294	295	Structural precast/stressed concrete units
9	290	295	Non-structural precast concrete components
10	270	271	Formwork
11	317	318	Brickwork and blockwork
12	376	381	Natural stone
13	315	318	Asphalt work
14	301	304	Slate and tile roofing
15	313	314	Asbestos cement sheet roofing and cladding
16	227	227	Plastic-coated steel sheet roofing and cladding
17	255	262	Aluminium sheet roofing and cladding
18	303	304	Built-up felt roofing
19	267	268	Built-up felt roofing on metal decking
20	256	256	Carpentry, manufactured boards and softwood flooring
21	290	291	Hardwood flooring
22	256	260	Tile and sheet flooring (vinyl etc)
23	244	248	Jointless flooring (epoxy resin type)
24	281	282	Softwood joinery
25	254	251	Hardwood joinery
26	279	282	Ironmongery
27	223	227	Steelwork
28	345	347	Steel windows and doors
29	313	319	Aluminium windows and doors
30	236	241	Miscellaneous metalwork
31	303	305	Cast-iron pipes and fittings
32	311	316	Plastic pipes and fittings
33	293	297	Copper tubes, fittings and cylinders
34	285	294	Mild steel pipes, fittings and tanks
35	275	280	Boilers, pumps and radiators
36	282	289	Sanitary fittings
37	260	285	Insulation
38	284	285	Plastering to walls and ceilings
39	295	295	Beds and screeds to floors, roofs and pavings
40	267	268	Dry partitions and linings
41	290	293	Tiling and terrazzo work
42	282	285	Suspended ceilings (dry construction)
43	276	278	Glass and mirrors
44	280	282	Decorations
45	256	262	Drainage pipework (other than cast iron)
46	241	246	Fencing, gates and screens
47	331	336	Bituminous surfacing to roads and paths
48	288	289	Soft landscaping
49	240	244	Lead work

Figure 20

(b) the total of items assigned to work categories included in the valuation before adjustment and the amount of the adjustment were then entered at Q and R on Form D (see p. 156). The total value to date of the balance of adjustable work was calculated from the valuation and entered on Form D and from this the balance of adjustable work for Valuation No. 12 was calculated by deducting the amount included in Valuation No. 11. The gross adjustment on the balance of adjustable work was then calculated, as indicated on Form D, and the amount entered in the space beneath the amount in respect of the work categories total. The sum of these two amounts (£1377) was the total of fluctuations for March using the provisional index numbers.

(c) at the same time as provisional index numbers for March became available, firm index numbers were published for December and so the fluctuations total included in Valuation No. 9, carried out on 23 December 1987, calculated on provisional index numbers, could then be adjusted. Accordingly, Form WC1/ WC2, used to record the provisional fluctuations calculation for each work category, was then filled in under the column heading 'Firm' (see p. 157). The firm index numbers for December were entered in the 'Index for Valuation Period' column and, in those cases where they differed from the provisional numbers, the revised amount of 'gross valuation including VOP' was calculated. Where there was no difference, the figures were simply carried over from column 5 to column 7. The revised amounts, as appropriate, were then entered on Form D (see p. 158) alongside the provisional ones and the difference in the totals at 'Y' and 'Z' (£34.00) was entered in the last space on the form as an addition for inclusion in Certificate No. 12.

It will be obvious from the foregoing, that it is essential that the record of calculations on Form WC1/WC2 and Form D should be carefully filed away after each valuation, along with Forms A and B.

The calculations described above are shown in Figure 21.

Form A

Allocation of bill of quantities items to work categories

Contract No. .... *265/6* ....   Employer *Skinton Development Co*

Project ... *Shops and Flats,* ...   Contractor *Beacon Ltd.*
.... *Thames Street, Skinton.* ....

		Bill of quantities Nos.	2 – 4
Cat. No.2/	Bill of quantities item reference		Amount £
1	*16A-F; 17A-D; 18A-H.*		5531
2	*20A – 23G; 109A-112C; 119A -119C; 122A-C; 140A-D.*		21960
3	*23H – 25C; 112D -114G; 119D-G.*		11553
4	*-*		-
5	*-*		-
6	*27A – 29B; 90A-D; 119H; 119K; 140E -141F*		25704
7	*29C – 30E; 90E- 91B;*		16214
8	*-*		-
9	*32A – 32K; 91C – 91F.*		4374
10	*31A – 31J; 91F - 91H; 119J; 142A-E.*		16564
11	*34A – 43D; 92A-D; 120A-D.*		46496
12	*-*		-
13	*-*		-
14	*-*		-
15	*-*		-
16	*-*		-
17	*-*		-
18	*-*		-
19	*-*		-
20	*45A – 46L.*		12652
21	*-*		-
22	*-*		-
23	*-*		-
24	*47A – 64D.*		36511
25	*66A – K.*		3560
26	*67A – 68N.*		1620

Total to overleaf £ | 202739

Figure 21

Form A (cont.)

	Total from overleaf £	202739
27	-	-
28	-	-
29	-	-
30	70A - 74G; 120E - 121H.	11311
31	-	-
32	76A - 77C; 78F - 79E.	5617
33	78A - E; 80A - F; 82C - L; 84E - 85G.	8866
34	81A - H; 82A - B.	1867
35	83A - K; 84A - D.	3983
36	87A - L.	6493
37	87M - 88C.	649
38	93A - 94C.	7049
39	94D - 94H; 142F - L.	9761
40	-	-
41	95A - 96F.	5439
42	-	-
43	98A - 101F.	8392
44	103A - 107C.	17264
45	114H - 118K.	10161
46	127A - 139J.	16776
47	141G - L.	5317
48	142M - S.	-

	Total £	321684
Provisional sums to which formula will apply		5000
	Total L £	326684
Provisional sums to which formula will not apply (including dayworks)	Total M £	12050
PC sums (including main contractor's profit)	Total N £	102524

Figure 21 (*cont.*)

Form B

(Part 1)   Summary of Form A

Contract No. ___265/6___   Employer ___Skinton Development Co.___

Project ___Shops and Flats,___   Contractor ___Beecon Ltd.___
___Thames Street, Skinton.___

Bill of quantities No.	Work allocated to categories and provisional sums to which formula will apply (Total L Form A)	Provisional sums to which formula will not apply (including daywork) (Total M Form A)	PC sums including main contractor's profit (Total N Form A)
1			
2			
3	326 684	12 050	102 524
4			
5			
6			
7			
Totals £	X 326 684	Y 12 050	Z 102 524

(Part 2)   Calculation of balance of adjustable work

		£	495 000
Contract sum (before deduction of credit for old materials)			
Deduct	(i) Provisional sums to which formula will not apply (including dayworks) — Total Y above £ 12 050		
	(ii) PC sums (including main contractor's profit) — Total Z above £ 102 524	114 574	
	Total of contract sum properly subject to price adjustment	£	370 426
Deduct	Value of work allocated to work categories, and provisional sums to which the formula will apply — Total X above	£	326 684
	Balance of adjustable work	£	53 742

Figure 21 (*cont.*)

Form WC1/WC2

Work Category Indices (Base Month) and Calculation of Gross Valuation

Base Month: JANUARY 1987		
Valuation No.	12	Date of Valuation: 25th March 1988
		for month of: March
Contract No.	265/6	
Project: Shops and Flats, Thames Street, Skinton.		

Work Category		Valuation this month (Q)	PROVISIONAL			FIRM		Work category No. 2/
No. 2/	Base Month Index		Index for valuation period	Gross valuation including VOP $(3 \times \frac{4}{2})(VT)$		Index for valuation period	Gross valuation including VOP $(5 \times \frac{6}{4})(VT)$	
1	2	£ 3	4	£ 5		6	£ 7	8
1	269	-	-	-				
2	266	-	-	-				
3	285	-	-	-				
6	275	1410	280	1436				
7	241	457	247	468				
9	281	-	-	-				
10	257	590	271	622				
11	301	2465	318	2604				
20	243	297	256	302				
24	270	2328	282	2431				
25	241	1551	251	1615				
26	270	341	282	356				
30	230	851	241	892				
32	290	241	316	263				
33	259	528	297	605				
34	275	-	-	-				
35	266	630	280	663				
36	267	1115	289	1207				
37	234	-	-	-				
38	271	1720	285	1809				
39	284	540	295	561				
41	275	-	-	-				
43	245	1446	278	1641				
44	268	4081	282	4294				
45	242	-	-	-				
46	231	530	246	564				
47	312	-	-	-				
48	266	-	-	-				
		21111	(Q) (VT)	22333		(VT)		Totals

Figure 21 *(cont.)*

Form D

Summary of price
adjustment calculations

Valuation No.	12	Date of Valuation: 25th March 1988
		for month of: March
Contract No.		265/6
Project: Shops and Flats, Thames Street, Skinton.		

Valuation this month   £ | 21111 | (Q)

BALANCE OF ADJUSTABLE WORK

Total to date   £ | 31793 |

Total from
previous valuation   £ | 29119 |

This valuation   £ | 2674 | (P)

	PRICE ADJUSTMENT DUE BASED ON	
	Provisional Indices £	Firm Indices £
Gross adjustment due (from WC2)(Total VT–Q) (R)	1222	
Gross adjustment on balance of adjustable work ($\frac{P}{Q}$ x R)	155	
Sub total	1377	
Deduct: Non-adjustable element %	–	–
Total provisional price adjustment due Carried forward to Certificate No. (Y) £	1377	////////
Total firm price adjustment due (Z) £		
Balance of firm price adjustment due Carried forward to Certificate No. Add/~~Deduct~~[†] £		

[†]Delete whichever is not applicable
If Y is >Z then DEDUCT
If Y is <Z then ADD

Figure 21 (*cont.*)

Form WC1/WC2

Work Category Indices (Base Month) and Calculation of Gross Valuation

Base Month: JANUARY 1987	Valuation No.	9	Date of Valuation: 23rd December 1987
			for month of: December
	Contract No.		265/6
	Project: Shops and Flats, Thames Street, Skinton.		

			PROVISIONAL		FIRM		
Work Category No. 2/	Base Month Index	Valuation this month (Q)	Index for valuation period	Gross valuation including VOP $(3\times\frac{4}{2})$(VT)	Index for valuation period	Gross valuation including VOP $(5\times\frac{6}{4})$(VT)	Work category No. 2/
1	2	£ 3	4	£ 5	6	£ 7	8
1	269						1
2	266						2
3	285						3
6	275	2232	278	2256	278	2256	6
7	241	1040	244	1053	244	1053	7
9	281	370	288	379	290	382	9
10	257	1650	270	1733	270	1733	10
11	301	4320	316	4535	317	4550	11
20	243	992	256	1045	256	1045	20
24	270	2840	281	2956	281	2956	24
25	241	-	-	-	-	-	25
26	270	360	279	372	279	372	26
30	230	-	-	-	-	-	30
32	290	230	311	247	311	247	32
33	259	520	290	582	293	588	33
34	275	-	-	-	-	-	34
35	266	590	275	610	275	610	35
36	267	560	283	593	282	591	36
37	234	-	-	-	-	-	37
38	271	1890	284	1981	284	1981	38
39	284	860	293	887	295	893	39
41	275	-	-	-	-	-	41
43	245	-	-	-	-	-	43
44	268	1720	280	1797	280	1797	44
45	242	-	-	-	-	-	45
46	231	750	240	779	241	782	46
47	312	-	-	-	-	-	47
48	266	-	-	-	-	-	48
		20924 (Q)	(VT)	21805	(VT)	21836	Totals

Figure 21 (*cont.*)

Form D

Summary of price
adjustment calculations

Valuation No.	9	Date of Valuation: 23rd December 1987
		for month of: December
Contract No.	265/6	
Project: Shops and Flats, Thames Street, Skinton.		

Valuation this month £ | 20 924 | (Q)

BALANCE OF ADJUSTABLE WORK

Total to date	£	22 010	
Total from previous valuation	£	20 035	
This valuation	£	1975	(P)

	PRICE ADJUSTMENT DUE BASED ON	
	Provisional Indices £	Firm Indices £
Gross adjustment due (from WC2)(Total VT–Q) (R)	881	912
Gross adjustment on balance of adjustable work ($\frac{P}{Q}$ x R)	83	86
Sub total	964	998
Deduct: Non-adjustable element %	–	–
Total provisional price adjustment due Carried forward to Certificate No (Y) £	964	///////
Total firm price adjustment due (Z) £		998
Balance of firm price adjustment due Carried forward to Certificate No Add/~~Deduct~~ £		34

†Delete whichever is not applicable
If Y is >Z then DEDUCT
If Y is <Z then ADD

Figure 21 (*cont.*)

REFERENCES

1. GOODACRE, P. E., *Formula Method of Price Adjustment for Building Contracts* (Reading: College of Estate Management, 1978), p. 81.
2. JCT, *Consolidated Main Contract Formula Rules* (London: RIBA Publications Ltd, 1987).
3. JCT, *Practice Note 17, Fluctuations* (London: RIBA Publications Ltd 1982), para. 8.
4. *Price Adjustment Formulae for Building Contracts (Series 2) Guide to application and procedure* (London: HMSO, 1977), p. 7.
5. *Price Adjustment Formulae for Building Contracts* (London: RICS, 1975), p. 8.
6. *Price Adjustment Formulae for Building Contracts (Series 2), op. cit.*
7. ibid.
8. ibid., p. 13.

11

Claims

Contractor's claims may be of three kinds:

1 Common law.
2 *Ex gratia*.
3 Contractual.

COMMON LAW CLAIMS

These arise from causes which are outside the express terms of a contract. They relate to breaches by the Employer or his agents of either implied, or express terms of the contract, e.g. if the Employer in some way hindered progress of the Works or if the architect were negligent in carrying out his duties, resulting in loss to the contractor.

EX GRATIA CLAIMS

These have no legal basis but are claims which the contractor considers the Employer has a moral duty to meet, e.g. if he has seriously underpriced an item whose quantity has been increased substantially because of a variation or the remeasurement of a provisional item, which will in consequence cause him considerable loss. The Employer is under no obligation to meet such 'hardship claims' but may be prepared to do so on grounds of natural justice or to help the contractor where otherwise he might be forced into liquidation.

CONTRACTUAL CLAIMS

These arise from express terms of a contract and form by far the most frequent kind of claim. They may relate to any or all of the following:

(a) fluctuations;
(b) variations;
(c) extensions of time;
(d) loss and/or expense due to matters affecting regular progress of the works.

Fluctuations claims

These relate to increases in the costs of labour, materials and plant and to levies, contributions and taxes, which the contract provides for the contractor to be reimbursed by the traditional method in clauses 38 and 39 of JCT 80. This has been fully explained in Chapter 9 and requires no further treatment here.

Claims arising from variations

These may relate to one or more of the following clauses:

(i) clause 13.5.1.2 – the PQS may have priced at bill rates variation items which are apparently similar to bill items but which were not executed under similar conditions to those envisaged at the time of tendering. For example, an Architect's Instruction changing the kind of facing bricks may affect the time taken for laying the bricks, and may lead to more sorting if there is a higher proportion of misshapen bricks or if they are more susceptible to damage in handling. The contractor would be entitled to an increase over the bill rates.

(ii) clause 13.5.3.3 – the contractor may claim that adjustment of one or more preliminary items should be made, though the PQS has not included the adjustment in his valuation of a variation. For example, an Architect's Instruction changing the pointing of faced brickwork from 'pointing as the work proceeds' to 'pointing on completion' may require scaffolding to be left standing for a longer period than would otherwise have been necessary. If scaffolding is priced in the Preliminaries (as is usual), the relevant item should be adjusted.

(iii) clause 13.5.5 – it may be claimed that, in consequence of a variation, the conditions under which other work is carried out has changed and therefore the bill rates for that work should be adjusted to reflect the changed conditions. Thus, a variation changing part of the foundations of a building from concrete deep strip to short bored piles would, it might be claimed, so reduce the total volume of concrete required for the rest of the deep strip foundations that the bill rates for the concrete would no longer apply. If this argument can be substantiated, the rates should be adjusted.

(iv) clause 13.5.6 – the contractor may claim that he has incurred additional costs which are directly associated with a variation but for which he has not been reimbursed by the application of the normal valuation rules. An example of such a claim is given on p. 108.

Claims for extensions of time

These arise from clause 25 of JCT 80. Clause 23 requires the contractor to complete the Works on or before the Date for Completion stated in the Appendix (see p. 235) or such later date as may be fixed by the architect under clauses 25 or 33. If the contractor fails to do so, he becomes liable for liquidated damages (clause 24), which the Employer is entitled to deduct from payments due to the contractor at the rate stated in the Appendix for the period between the date when completion should have taken place and when it actually took place. This action of the Employer is subject to the prior issue by the architect of a certificate of non-completion by the completion date.

The rate of liquidated damages stated in the Appendix should be a genuine pre-estimate of the likely loss to the Employer due to the time overrun and is not adjustable according to the actual loss incurred. The purpose of granting extension(s) of time is only to relieve the contractor of liability to pay liquidated damages for the period of the extension and does not carry an automatic right to reimbursement of any loss or expense which the contractor may claim he has suffered or incurred due to the matter for which the extension was granted.

Clause 25.4 lists Relevant Events, the happening of any one of which is a ground for extending the contract time by such period(s) of time as the architect estimates is 'fair and reasonable', if it is 'apparent that the progress of the Works is being or is likely to be delayed'. The contractor must give prompt written notice of such actual or likely delay, (i) stating the cause(s), (ii) identifying the Relevant Events, (iii) giving particulars of the expected effects, and (iv) the estimated extent of the delay in the completion of the Works. The architect is under no obligation to act until such notice has been received.

Within 12 weeks of receipt of all the above information, the architect must give a fair and reasonable extension of time if he is of the opinion that the cause of delay is a Relevant Event and that completion of the Works is likely to be delayed thereby. If an Architect's Instruction calls for the omission of work, the architect may fix an earlier completion date than that fixed on a previous occasion, provided it is not earlier than the Date for Completion stated in the Appendix.

After the completion date, if that occurs before actual completion, the architect must review his previous decisions (if any) on extensions, not later than the end of 12 weeks after the date of actual completion. He must then (i) fix a later completion date, (ii) fix an earlier completion date, or (iii) confirm the completion date previously fixed and notify his decision to the contractor in writing.

Claims for loss and/or expense due to matters affecting regular progress

These claims arise under clauses 26 or 34 of JCT 80. Clause 26.2 lists eight matters (in addition to deferment of giving possession of the site to the contractor) which might materially affect progress. If the contractor believes that any one or more of those matters has affected the regular progress of the Works and that he has, in consequence, incurred loss and/or expense, then he may apply in writing to the architect for reimbursement. If the architect is of the opinion that such loss and expense has been or is likely to be incurred due to one or more of the stated matters, he must ascertain or (as normally happens) he must ask the PQS to ascertain the amount of such loss and expense which has been or is being incurred.

All the matters listed in clause 26.2 are those for which the Employer is responsible, being acts or omissions of the Employer or the architect as his agent. Excluded from recovery are all other causes of loss or expense, such as those which are unknown or undefined or the result of commercial risks, bad pricing of the contractor's tender, bad weather or bad organization or management of the contract. Nor is there any automatic right of recovery of loss solely because an extension of time has been granted. On the other hand, it is possible for the contractor to have suffered recoverable loss or expense when no extension of time has been granted.

The architect need take no action unless and until a written application which clearly states the circumstances which have caused the loss has been received from the contractor. A telephone request or an oral application made to the architect on the site is insufficient; also a new application is necessary for each new matter that arises. If the architect fails to act upon receipt of an application properly made, the Employer will become in breach of contract and liable for damages.

The contractor is not required to formulate a claim but must provide all necessary information to enable the amount of the loss or expense to be ascertained. This means that the contractor must be prepared to reveal what he probably considers to be confidential information about such matters as actual wages and bonuses paid to operatives, details of head office overheads, etc. 'Ascertain' means 'to find out exactly', so it is necessary for the PQS to find out the actual loss and not to rely upon estimates or the use of formulae in order to arrive at a sum.

The loss and/or expense, to be recoverable, must have been a direct consequence of the matter(s) referred to in the claim without there having been any intervening cause. Thus, if the Employer fails to provide materials for the Works which he has agreed to provide and the contractor is asked to obtain them, then the contractor is entitled to recover the expense incurred in so doing, as well as the loss due to delay in obtaining them. If, however, in obtaining those supplies, deliveries are held up because of a strike in the haulage industry and additional loss or expense ensues, this would not be recoverable, being an indirect result of the original cause.

If the contractor does formulate a claim or even if he just provides required information, he is much more likely to succeed in his claim if he makes a clear and orderly presentation of the data. It will not help the architect in forming an opinion as to the soundness of a claim or the PQS in ascertaining the proper amount if they are presented with a jumbled mass of papers which it is virtually impossible to sort out.

Heads of claim may be any or all of the following:

(i) inefficient use of labour and/or plant;

(ii) increases in costs of labour, materials, etc. during the period of disruption;

(iii) site running costs;

(iv) head office overheads;

(v) finance charges and interest;

(vi) loss of profit.

(i) Inefficient use of labour and/or plant refers to men and plant standing idle or working at a reduced level of output. It would be necessary for the contractor in substantiating a claim to produce evidence of the estimated levels of output used in preparing his tender and records of the actual output during the disruption period.

(ii) Increases in costs would normally only apply in the case of firm price contracts, although they could possibly apply in the case of fluctuations contracts using clauses 38 or 39, in respect of materials, etc. not listed on the list of basic prices of materials.

(iii) Site running costs relate to site staff costs, offices, mess-rooms, sheds, rates on temporary buildings, etc., normally referred to as preliminaries. Prolongation of a contract could result in some or all of these items being required for a period in excess of that for which the contractor allowed in his tender.

(iv) Head office overheads include the cost of maintaining head and branch offices, plant and materials yards, rents, rates, directors' and staff salaries, office running expenses, travelling expenses, professional fees and depreciation. Because of the complexity of trying to sort out such costs, a formula is often used as a means of evaluation. Three in common use are Hudson's, Emden's and the Eichleay formula.[1] The first two are similar:

$$\frac{h}{100} \times \frac{c}{cp} \times pd$$

where h = head office overheads and profit per cent included in the contract (Hudson's), or h = per cent arrived at by dividing total overhead costs and profit of the contractor's organization as a whole by total turnover (Emden's); c = contract sum; cp = contract period in weeks; and pd = period of delay in weeks.

Many PQSs do not accept the use of formulae on the grounds that actual cost only is admissible and that the contractor must specify precisely what actual additional expense has been incurred.[2] The decision in *Tate & Lyle Food Distribution Co Ltd v Greater London Council (1982) 1 WLR 149* supports this view.

(v) Finance charges or interest – finance charges are interest charges incurred by the contractor on money he has had to borrow (or interest that he was prevented from earning on his own capital) in order to finance the direct loss and/or expense claimed. The rates of such interest must be those actually paid to the bank or other finance source and certified by the contractor's auditors. Interest due to late payment of sums owing (such as retention monies) is not admissible.

(vi) Loss of profit refers to profit which the contractor could have earned but was prevented from earning as a direct result of one or more of the matters listed in clause 26.2. This could arise where the architect omitted a substantial part of the project, say one wing of a new hospital. In such a case, the contractor would be entitled to reimbursement of the profit which he could prove he would have made had he been allowed to complete the contract as originally envisaged. It might also happen that because of prolongation of one contract, the contractor was prevented from taking on another. If he could prove his loss of profit as arising directly from a clause 26 matter, he would be entitled to reimbursement.

It should be noted that acceleration costs, i.e. additional costs incurred due to speeding up progress of a contract in order to meet the completion date, are not recoverable, nor are the costs of preparing a claim or providing detailed information to enable loss or expense to be ascertained.[3]

Having ascertained 'from time to time' amounts of loss and expense incurred, the architect is required to include them in the next interim certificate after each ascertainment. Such amounts should be paid in full, i.e. they are not subject to retention. They will also be included in the final account for adjustment of the contract sum.

The provisions of clause 34 in regard to loss and/or expense incurred as a result of disruption following the finding of antiquities, fossils, etc. are similar to the provisions in clause 26. The main difference is that the contractor is not required to give written notice to the architect as a pre-condition to consideration of a claim, he is merely required to inform him and to await his instructions.

REFERENCES

1. R. KNOWLES, Calculating office overheads, *Chartered Quantity Surveyor*, 1985, Vol. 8, No. 5, p. 207.
2. R. MORLEDGE, Letter, *Chartered Quantity Surveyor*, 1986, Vol. 8, No. 7, p. 5.
3. RICS, *Contractor's Direct Loss and/or Expense* (London: Surveyors Publications, 1987), p. 11.

12

Interim valuations

When the value of contracts is more than a few thousand pounds, it is normal practice for contractors to be paid sums on account as the construction work proceeds. This is because it is generally recognized that it would be unreasonable to expect contractors to finance construction operations without assistance from Employers. Also, the expense of borrowing large sums, which otherwise would be involved, would add significantly to total costs – which it is in the interest of Employers to minimize. All the Standard Forms include provisions for periodic or 'interim' payments to be made for these reasons.

It is universally accepted that interim payments are approximate only and, provided the amounts included for the various constituents are reasonable, no objection will be raised because they are not exact. For this reason, the amounts shown in certificates are always round pounds, as also are the sums in the main money column of valuations.

FREQUENCY OF VALUATIONS AND 'VALUATION DATE'

Clause 30 of the JCT Form provides for the Employer to pay the contractor such sums as are stated to be due in Interim Certificates issued by the architect at the periods stated in the Appendix to the Conditions of Contract. In practice, this normally means monthly, commencing one month after the date on which the contractor takes possession of the site. The architect usually relies on the quantity surveyor to advise him as to the sum which should be stated as due in any such certificate. In order to do this, the PQS prepares a valuation in accordance with the provisions of clause 30 of the JCT Form.

As an alternative to regular monthly certificates, the contract conditions may provide for 'stage payments',[1] i.e. for payments to be made when certain defined stages in the construction work have been completed. Thus, the first payment may be due when the substructure is finished and ground slabs laid, the second when superstructure walls and upper floors are constructed, the third when the roof is finished, and so on. Stage payments are more appropriate to housing contracts than to more complex projects where the stages are often not so readily or satisfactorily definable. Table 1 shows a breakdown of a housing contract, consisting of four types of house, into stages in preparation for interim valuations.

Table 1 Typical breakdown of house type contract sums for use in 'stage payments' method of interim valuations

Stages	*Proportion of contract value for house types*				Totals
	A	B	C	D	
	£	£	£	£	£
Substructure	2 300	2 480	2 392	2 852	10 024
External walls, upper floors, windows and external doors	6 780	7 868	7 164	8 856	30 668
Roof, internal walls and partitions, first fixings	5 874	6 720	6 256	7 954	26 804
Plumbing, internal finishings, second fixings	7 486	8 332	7 904	8 432	32 154
External works	2 480	2 912	2 770	4 360	12 522
Preliminaries	3 700	3 964	3 838	4 704	16 206
Totals	28 620	32 276	30 324	37 158	128 378

As the sum eventually certified as due for payment relates to work actually completed and unfixed materials and goods actually stored on the site, it is necessary for the PQS personally to visit the site to see for himself both the completed work and the unfixed materials and goods and then to ascertain their total value.

Where the contract provides for advances at regular intervals, it will be advantageous to decide from the start a fixed date in each month on which to do valuations. Although the PQS has no obligation under the terms of the JCT Form to notify the contractor when he proposes to visit the site for valuation purposes, nevertheless it is desirable as well as courteous to do so and even better if the PQS and the contractor's surveyor agree on a 'valuation date' in each month.

From the contractor's point of view, the exact position of the day in the month may well affect his cash flow as, for example, his invoices for materials become payable at the end of the month. Also, if the NEDO formula method of recovery of fluctuations applies (see p. 146), the fluctuations amount included in a valuation will be affected by the relationship between the 'valuation date' and the date of publication of the monthly indices.

From the Employer's point of view the 'valuation date' will affect his cash flow situation also. If the Employer is a public authority and it is necessary for payments to be approved by a finance committee, then the date of the committee meeting in each month may have a direct bearing upon when the valuation ought to be done, if payment is not to be delayed unduly. The PQS should give careful consideration to any such factors involved, including his own commitments in regard to other contracts already running.

GENERAL PROCEDURE

The proper way to prepare an interim valuation is to value, on each occasion, the amount of work which has been done since the beginning of the contract and the value of unfixed materials and goods on the site on the 'valuation date'. From the total value so arrived at, the total of previous payments on account, if any, will be deducted, leaving a balance due for payment. By following this procedure strictly, any under-valuation or over-valuation of either work completed or of unfixed materials on the last 'valuation date' will be automatically corrected. The surveyor should not attempt to value in isolation the work done and the materials delivered since the last valuation.

Experience will confirm that valuations are most conveniently set out on double billing paper, thus allowing for sub-totals to each section and subdivision being carried over into the right-hand money column (*see* example on p. 185). Such sub-totals are often useful for carrying forward into subsequent valuations.

Preparing the valuation on site

The surveyor's first task on visiting the site for valuation purposes (having first made his presence known to the site agent), is to tour the Works, making notes as necessary of the extent of work done and listing the quantities of the various materials and goods stored on the site. He will then be in a position to get down to preparing a draft valuation in the site agent's or clerk of works' office (if there is no office for the PQS's exclusive use, as often there is not). It is highly desirable, if at all possible that the valuation total be determined before leaving the site.

As already stated, the PQS and contractor's surveyor will usually agree to meet on site at a mutually convenient time on the 'valuation date' in the month and will prepare the valuation together, although of course, the responsibility for the resulting recommendation to the architect will be that of the PQS alone. Thus, the total sum and its constituent amounts will normally be agreed before leaving the site and subsequent dispute will be avoided. Sometimes, the contractor's surveyor is happy to leave valuations entirely to the PQS and will accept whatever amounts the architect certifies.

Some contractors prefer to prepare detailed applications for interim payments themselves which they submit to the PQS a few days before the valuation date. The PQS has no obligation, however, to make use of them, although he may find it convenient to use them as a basis for his own valuation by checking each of the constituent amounts and, if necessary, amending any as he sees fit.

Even when such detailed applications are not made, it may be very helpful to have a list, prepared beforehand by the site agent, of the quantities of unfixed materials stored on site. PQSs often arrange with contractors for such a list to be available when they arrive on site to prepare the valuation. The PQS should then check the list, including the quantities, when making his initial tour of the Works.

Inclusions in valuations

Clause 30.2 of the JCT Form provides that 'the amount stated as due in an Interim Certificate . . . shall be the gross valuation' of specified constituent parts of the Works, less the Retention

Percentage and the total of previous interim certificates. In order to determine 'the gross valuation', the value of each of the constituent parts has to be ascertained. Those parts may be any or all of the following:

1   Preliminaries.
2   Main contractor's work (as billed).
3   Variations.
4   Unfixed materials and goods.
5   Statutory fees and charges.
6   Nominated sub-contractors' work.
7   Nominated suppliers' goods.
8   Fluctuations in costs of labour, materials and/or taxes, etc.
9   Retention.

Each of the items on the above list will now be considered in detail. The examples at the end of the chapter illustrate the application of most of the principles and procedures discussed.

1. Preliminaries

Where there is a bill of quantities, the evaluation of the preliminaries will usually be less difficult than where there is not. In the latter case, it will be necessary, before the date of the first valuation, to make an apportionment of the contract sum to each of its principal constituents. The preliminaries constituent will then need to be broken down into separate amounts such as would normally be seen in the preliminaries section of a bill of quantities. This process will be very much easier and the results be more satisfactory, if there is a Contract Sum Analysis (see p. 69) which shows the total of Preliminaries included in the tender. The contractor will be able to produce his build-up of the tender and the individual amounts allowed in it for the main Preliminaries items. These amounts will then be available for valuation purposes – and later, for the adjustment of Preliminaries, if necessary, in the final account – just as if there had been a bill of quantities.

Even where there is a bill, the situation may still present difficulties. The contractor may have put amounts against all, some, one or none of the priceable items in the Preliminaries section, having included the balance of their value, if any, in other parts of the bill. The surveyor can only take account, of course, of those items which have been priced, even though they may represent only part of the total cost of the Preliminaries. It will help in arriving at realistic valuations if the sums which have been inserted in the Preliminaries section are analysed, their constituent parts being dealt with as described in the following paragraphs. Again, such analyses will be more satisfactory if provided by or agreed with the contractor, preferably before the contract is signed.

Preliminaries items are of four kinds, namely, cost-related, time-related, single-payment or a combination of two or more of the others. Those which are cost-related (e.g. Water for the Works) depend for their value on that of the remainder of the contract sum or of its labour content. Time-related items (e.g. site supervision) depend for their value on the contract period. Single-payment items (e.g. the provision of temporary access roads) are those whose value is not affected either by the value of the rest of the contract or by the contract period but are carried out at a particular point in the progress of the Works. The cost of some Preliminaries items consists of one or two single-payment components and a time-related one, e.g. the provision of a tower crane, involving single payments for erection and dismantling and a weekly hire charge for the intervening period.

The surveyor's next task prior to the first valuation, after having ascertained, where appropriate, the breakdown of the Preliminaries items which have been priced, is to put them into the categories described above, so that the total of each category is then readily available for each valuation thereafter. Table 3 illustrates how this may be done.

It is not uncommon to deal with the total value of the Preliminaries as if the items were either all cost-related or all time-related.[2] Thus, in the first case, the total of the Preliminaries is calculated as a percentage of the contract sum after deducting the Preliminaries and the prime cost sums. In each valuation, this percentage is applied to the total value of item 2 of the list on p. 172. In the second case, the total of the Preliminaries is divided by the contract period (in months) and the resulting sum is multiplied by the number of months which have elapsed to date. This amount is then included in the valuation as the total amount for Preliminaries.

There is no practical reason why the Preliminaries should not be dealt with in either of these two ways, although it should be

Table 2 Breakdown of Preliminaries items. Five-storey block of shops and flats in Thames Street, Skinton*

Items	Cost-related	Time-related	Lump sums (a)	(b)	Totals
	£	£	£	£	£
Plant and scaffolding	2 700	900	550	350	4 500
Welfare	–	2 880	450	270	3 600
Setting out	–	–	540	–	540
Foreman and supervision	–	20 000	–	–	20 000
Watching and lighting	–	1 350	–	–	1 350
Electric lighting and power	–	180	–	–	180
Temporary roads	–	–	1 170	180,	1 350
Site huts	–	720	270	90	1 080
Site telephones	–	450	–	–	450
Site fencing and hoardings	–	270	1 080	270	1 620
Drying out	–	–	–	450	450
Cleaning out	–	–	–	540	540
Insurance against injury	3 632	–	–	–	3 632
All Risks insurance	811	–	–	–	811
Water for the Works	1 260	–	117	–	1 377
Totals	8 403	26 750	4 177	2 150	41 480

Notes: Total of cost-related amounts = 2.50 per cent of Contract Sum less p.c. sums and Preliminaries.

Total of time-related amounts = £1337 per month for the Contract Period of 20 months.

Lump sums (a) are sums expended at or soon after the commencement of the contract for erection, installing, etc.

Lump sums (b) are sums expended mainly towards the end of the contract for dismantling, removal, etc.

*See Appendix A for full details of the Contract.

recognized that they give only approximate results. It is argued in their defence that these methods save time, although it should be pointed out that once the allocation of amounts to the four categories as illustrated in Table 2 has been done, it takes very little longer each month to calculate more nearly the true value.

The objection to both these methods is that they result in overpayment of some items and and underpayment of others. Also, where the time-related method is used and the contract runs behind schedule, there will be a danger of overpayment, unless the fixed monthly amounts are adjusted. Where the cost-related method is used, there is a danger of inadvertently exceeding the total of the Preliminaries when the total value of the contractor's own work has been significantly increased by variations.

None of the foregoing objections matters very much when the contract is keeping to schedule and no real problems arise. They will matter, however, if the employment of the contractor is determined because of his insolvency. Then, the likelihood will be that the Preliminaries will have been overpaid, particularly if the contract is in its early stages. The possibility of such embarrassment to the PQS (to put it at its best) will be avoided if the small amount of extra time and trouble is taken to ascertain more exactly the value of the Preliminaries.

2. Main contractor's work

The value of the work carried out by the contractor's own workforce will be readily ascertainable from the measured work sections of the bills of quantities or, in the case of lump sum contracts without quantities, from the Contract Sum Analysis, if provided, or from a schedule drawn up on the basis of an analysis of the tender. The prices contained in the bills of quantities, being 'the Contract Bills',[3] must be used, of course, in the valuation of the main contractor's work, regardless of whether the contractor under-priced or over-priced the work when compiling the tender.

The surveyor, when valuing the main contractor's work, will begin with the 'Excavation and Earthwork' section (or the Demolitions or Works on Site Bill if there is one or both) and proceed in order through all the succeeding work sections which contain items of work which have been wholly or partly carried out. He should put down separately the total valuation of such work within each work section or sub-section, indicating by use of bill item references what is included in each amount. The reason for so doing is that every amount can then be verified and substantiated subsequently, should any query arise. Also, such detail will often prove useful when doing the next valuation. Of course, if the whole of a work section has been completed, it is only necessary to show its total. The examples of valuations given at the end of the chapter illustrate the procedure.

The notes made during the initial tour and inspection of the Works will again be used in assessing approximately the value of any partly completed items, sections or sub-sections. The completed work as a percentage of the whole item should be indicated opposite the bill reference. Actual measurement of the work on site will seldom, if ever, be necessary solely for interim valuation purposes, except in the case of contracts not based on bills of quantities.

3. Variations

Very few projects, if any, have no variations. On some jobs they number in double or even treble figures. They present a difficulty in the context of interim valuations for several reasons. First, clause 30.2.1.1 of the JCT Form requires that effect be given in Interim Certificates to 'the measurement and valuation' of variations. For this to be done, each variation must be valued, either approximately or accurately, as soon as possible after issue. Pressure of other work may cause delay in dealing with variations but it may be dangerous to have to resort to guesswork in consequence. It is wise, therefore, to give priority to them, even if only to the extent of an approximate evaluation of the nett effect of each variation, before each valuation date. The methods of valuing variations are discussed in Chapter 8.

Secondly, the question of how best to deal with the effects of omissions on the measured sections of the bills of quantities is bound to arise. There are two alternatives. The first is to ignore the variations when dealing with the work measured in the bills, the omissions being allowed for when adding the nett value of variations. The second is to take the omissions into account when valuing 'main contractor's work' and adding the value of additions only against the 'variations' subhead.

In practice, a combination of the two alternatives will serve best. The first may be used as a general rule, the second being used where a complete section or group of items in the bills is affected by a variation. For example, a variation increasing the width of some (but not all) of the windows will affect part of the items for lintels, cavity trays, sills, window boards, etc. In such a case, it will probably be simpler to include the full value of the items as originally billed in the value of 'main contractor's work', leaving the nett value of the variation to take care of the omissions.

If, however, a variation is ordered changing the specification of all the internal doors from painted plywood-faced to hardwood-veneered and the linings and architraves from softwood to hardwood, then the second alternative will probably be preferable, that is, to exclude the whole of the appropriate sub-sections of the Woodwork section of the bills from the value of 'main contractor's work' and include in the 'variations' part of the valuation, the total value of the additions items.

4. Unfixed materials and goods

Clause 30.2.1.2 of the JCT Form requires the inclusion in the amount of an interim certificate of materials and goods delivered to the site for incorporation in the Works. In order to value them, the surveyor will need to be satisfied that the materials and goods are actually on the site and to ascertain approximately how much of each material or good there is. It is not necessary to know the exact quantities because by the time the next valuation is done, most or all of the materials will have been incorporated into finished work which will then be valued as such.

It is helpful if the contractor's surveyor prepares a list of all the materials with their respective quantities, immediately prior to the valuation date and has supporting delivery notes and invoices available so that each of the materials can be valued at invoice cost. The PQS will have then only to check that the materials and goods are on site and that the quantities and value are as stated. If not, he will amend the list accordingly. The most recent deliveries will probably not have been invoiced as yet and the costs of the equivalent types and qualities on the latest available invoices will be used instead.

It will be necessary to reduce or exclude the invoice value of (a) insufficiently protected materials or those which have deteriorated or been damaged; (b) quantities which are clearly in excess of requirements and (c) any materials or goods which have been delivered prematurely, that is, when the length of time before they are likely to be required is unreasonably long.

The JCT Form includes a provision in clause 30.3 for the value of materials and goods intended for the Works but not yet delivered to the site to be included in the certificate amount at the discretion of the architect, subject to a number of extra conditions. Briefly, these are: (a) that they are intended for incorporation into the Works and are in accordance with the contract, and that they need only be transported to the site to be ready for use; (b) that they are set apart at the place where they are being kept and are clearly identifiable and appropriately marked; (c) that ownership is established in written contracts or sub-contracts for their supply, and (*d*) that they are properly and adequately insured. The PQS must satisfy himself that all these conditions have been met before he accepts a claim for the value of the goods to be included in a valuation.

The question whether to allow for overheads and profit on the value of unfixed materials and goods sometimes arises. This may at first appear to be a reasonable suggestion, as the value of each part of the Works is presumed to include those factors and the materials and goods are to become part of the Works. It may appear also as a reasonable interpretation of the words 'total value' in clause 30.2.1.2. The Q.S. (Practice and Management) Committee of the Royal Institution of Chartered Surveyors has expressed the opinion that 'the word "total" is used only to indicate the collective value of work executed and materials delivered . . .' and 'could not be interpreted as including anything in addition to their value *for the purpose of the interim certificate*'.[4]

5. Statutory fees and charges

Any sums paid by the contractor to any local authority or statutory undertaker in respect of fees or charges for work executed or materials or goods supplied in the course of carrying out its statutory obligations should be included in the next interim valuation thereafter. Such charges would commonly be for connections to water, gas, and electricity mains.

Normally, there will be provisional or prime cost sums included in the bills of quantities in respect of such work and any sums for profit and attendances attached to the prime cost sums will be applied to the authorities' charges as in the case of nominated sub-contractors. It should be noted, however, that clause 6.3 of the JCT Form specifically excludes the operation of clause 35 to work done by statutory bodies. In consequence, there will be no question of adding any sums equivalent to cash discounts to the invoiced amounts, which invariably will be nett. This exclusion only applies to work done or goods supplied in discharge of the statutory obligations of the authorities. It does not apply to such work or goods which are outside the scope of those obligations, such as where they have been tendered for in competition with other sub-contractors and/or suppliers.

6. Nominated sub-contractors' work

Clause 21 of the JCT Nominated Sub-Contract NSC/4 spells out in detail what should be included in respect of sub-contract works. It is common practice for nominated sub-contractors to make application from time to time, through the main contractor, for the amounts on account to which they consider they are entitled.

It will be to the advantage of all concerned therefore, if nominated sub-contractors were informed at the commencement of the contract, or as soon thereafter as reasonably possible, of the valuation date in each month and asked to make applications for payments on account in time for inclusion in the next valuation. Then, in each case, if the surveyor is satisfied that work to the value stated has been carried out and materials to the value stated are stored on the site, he can include the amount applied for in his calculations. Profit and attendance additions should be made *pro rata* to the appropriate items in the bills of quantities, as explained in Chapter 7. Of course, if the work of any sub-contractor were complete, the full amount of attendances would be included. As in the valuation of main contractor's work, the sums included for nominated sub-contractors' work should be the total value of the whole of their work carried out to date, not for work done during the preceding month only.

Clause 35.13.3 of the JCT Form requires the contractor to provide proof of payment to any nominated sub-contractor of any sum included in the immediately preceding certificate in respect of their work, materials or goods. The standard valuation form (see p. 186) published by the Royal Institution of Chartered Surveyors has a footnote saying 'It is assumed that the architect/C.A. will . . . satisfy himself that previous payments directed for nominated Sub-contractors have been discharged'. Nevertheless, it is considered to be good practice to agree with the contractor at the first meeting for valuation purposes, that he will produce on each valuation date, proof of payment of all such amounts previously certified.[5] Should such proof not be forthcoming in respect of any sum the PQS should inform the architect/C.A. accordingly, so that he may proceed in the manner prescribed in clause 35.13.5 of the JCT Form.

Notwithstanding the absence of such proof, if the architect is satisfied that the contractor has properly discharged all amounts to a sub-contractor that have been included in previous certificates, then the prescribed default procedure will not be implemented (*see* clause 35.13.4 of the JCT Form).

If for that (or some other) reason, the Employer has paid a nominated sub-contractor direct, the contractor will still be entitled to the appropriate sums for profit and attendance. He will not be entitled, however, to any sum equal to the cash discount, as (*a*) he has not paid the subcontractor, and (*b*) the entitlement has been lost because of failure to pay within the period stipulated in clause 21.3.1.1 of the JCT Nominated Sub-Contract NSC/4. In the preparation of subsequent valuations, the total value of the sub-contractor's work should be shown in the normal way, plus profit and attendances. The deduction of the amount paid direct should be made, not by the PQS or the architect, but by the Employer.

Payments on account to nominated sub-contractors should include the value of unfixed materials on the same conditions as apply to the main contractor's materials (*see* clause 21.4 of the JCT Nominated Sub-Contract NSC/4). Another inclusion may be payments in respect of fluctuations. Whether a sub-contractor is entitled to fluctuations payments depends upon the terms of the sub-contract. If he is, then the calculation of the sums due will normally (but not necessarily)[6] be made in the same manner as is applicable to such sums due to the main contractor in respect of his own work. Profit and discount amounts should be calculated on the *total* payments to sub-contractors, including any fluctuations.

7. Nominated suppliers' goods

The value of goods and/or materials supplied by nominated suppliers should be included in valuations on the same basis as those supplied by non-nominated suppliers, namely, that the goods or materials are properly protected and stored whilst still unfixed and are not damaged or defective. Amounts should be inclusive of the proper discount for cash,[7] also for packing, carriage and delivery. Amounts should be exclusive of any trade discount allowed.

Where an invoice includes increases over the sum(s) stated in the quotation on which the order was based, whether such increases are admissible or not will depend on (a) the cause, and (*b*) the conditions of the contract of sale as stated in the quotation. If the cause is the imposition or increase of a tax or duty, the appropriate amount of the increase is admissible.[8] If the increase arises from some other cause, it will normally only be acceptable if the quotation specifically included a provision for such increased charges to be added.

8. Fluctuations in costs of labour, materials, etc.

The amounts, if any, under this heading which should be included in interim valuations, will vary according to whether the contract is a firm price or fluctuating price one (see p. 133 for definitions of these terms). The subject of fluctuations has been dealt with in detail in Chapters 9 and 10 and it will suffice to add only two further points here. First, where the 'traditional' method of recovery is allowed for in the contract conditions, amounts due should be included in interim valuations as early as possible after the costs have been incurred. Secondly, the amounts of fluctuations calculated by that method are payable in full (that is, they are not subject to retention) with the percentage addition (if any) referred to in clause 39.8 of the JCT Form and as stated in the Appendix to the Conditions of the contract. It should be noted, however, that amounts calculated by the 'Formula Rules' method are subject to retention (*see* clause 30.2.1.1 of the JCT Form).

9. Retention

It is a common provision in all the standard forms of building contract for a percentage of the valuation total to be deducted. Thus, the sum of money deducted is said to be 'retained' by the Employer and is called 'the Retention' in the JCT Form. The percentage used to calculate the amount of the Retention is called 'the Retention Percentage' (see clause 30.4.1.1).

The purpose in retaining part of the total value of work completed to date is (*a*) to provide an incentive for the contractor to complete the Works promptly, and (*b*) to 'cushion' the Employer to some extent against the effects of the contractor defaulting, should that happen.

The actual percentage retained will be that stated in the contract Conditions. Clause 30.4.1.1 and the Appendix to the JCT Form (*see* p. 236) provide for 5 per cent unless a lower rate is specified, and in a footnote to clause 30.4.1.1, the document says 'Where the Employer at the tender stage estimates the Contract

Sum to be £500,000 or over, the Retention Percentage should not be more than 3 per cent'.

The exclusions from the application of the retention percentage where the JCT Form applies are set out in clause 30.2.2. For convenience of reference, they are listed as follows:

(*a*) statutory fees and charges (clause 6.2);

(*b*) the cost of correcting any errors in setting out the Works, for which the contractor is not held responsible (clause 7);

(*c*) the cost of opening up work which has been covered up and/or the cost of testing materials, goods or executed work (clause 8.3);

(*d*) costs relating to patent rights (clause 9.2);

(*e*) the cost of making good faulty work for which the contractor is not held responsible (clauses 17.2 and 17.3);

(*f*) insurance premiums payable by the contractor in order to maintain insurances against damage to property other than the Works (clause 21.2.3);

(*g*) insurance premiums which should have been paid by the Employer but in regard to which he has defaulted (clauses 22B and 22C);

(*h*) loss or expense due to the regular progress of the Works having been affected by specified matters (clauses 26.1 and 34.3);

(*i*) final payments to nominated sub-contractors (clause 35.17);

(*j*) fluctuations in the cost of labour and materials, etc., calculated other than by the 'Formula Rules' method (clauses 38 and 39).

The JCT Form provides in clause 30.4 for one-half of the total then retained to be paid to the contractor in the next interim certificate after the architect has issued a Certificate of Practical Completion, subject, of course, to any releases of retention already made. Footnote [t] on p. 40 of the JCT Form makes this clear.

The same provision will operate under clause 18 of the JCT Form, should the Employer take possession of any part of the Works before the Date for Completion stated in the Appendix to the Conditions of the contract. In that circumstance, the amount of retention monies released will be one-half of that proportion of the total retention which the estimated value of 'the relevant part' bears to the total value of the Works.

The second half of the retention monies is released when the Defects Liability Period stated in the Appendix to the JCT Form has expired and the contractor has made good, at the architect's request, such defects as have appeared during that time. A similar provision applies to any part of the Works of which the Employer has taken early possession.

The architect may, if he so wishes, subject to certain conditions, release the whole of that part of the retention monies which relates to any nominated sub-contractor's work, at any time after Practical Completion of the sub-contract work. This action becomes obligatory upon the expiry of twelve months from the certified date of Practical Completion of the sub-contract work. The reason for this is that it is unreasonable that a nominated sub-contractor who completes his work early in the contract period, should have to wait many months for the payment of the balance due to him.

It will be seen from the above, that it is possible, at a particular 'valuation date', for the value of part of the Contract Works to be subject to the full retention percentage, that of another part to be subject to half that percentage, and the rest not to be subject to any retention at all. The PQS must be careful to ensure that the correct retention is deducted from those parts of the total value, and only those parts, to which it properly applies.

Sometimes, contractors object to retention being deducted from the value of goods and services for which they are obliged to pay in full, for example, materials and goods supplied by nominated suppliers (clause 36.4.6 of the JCT Form allows deduction of cash discount only). Whilst this situation may appear to be unfair to contractors, the proper action under the JCT Form is for the PQS to deduct retention from the whole of a valuation, less only amounts coming within the exclusions listed on p. 182.

NOTIFYING THE ARCHITECT

When the PQS has completed his valuation, he must inform the architect as soon as possible of the amount of the payment recommended. Prompt notification is essential if the architect's certificate is to be issued within the period from the valuation date prescribed in clause 30.2 of the JCT Form, that is, seven days. The Royal Institution of Chartered Surveyors publishes a standard form for this purpose in sets of three forms (one copy each for architect, contractor, and PQS) in pads of 100 sets. The form is shown in Figure 23, completed to correspond with the first of the examples of draft valuations.

The form provides for the totals only of (a) the gross valuation;

(*b*) retention; (*c*) amounts included in previous *certificates*; and (*d*) balance due for payment. Supporting information which should accompany the valuation recommendation are details of payments included in respect of nominated sub-contractors' work and full details of the retention deductions made. A standard form for this purpose also is published by the Royal Institution of Chartered Surveyors. Examples of its use are given in Figures 24, 27 and 30. The detailed build-up of valuations is not normally sent to the architect.

LIQUIDATED AND ASCERTAINED DAMAGES

It should be understood that no deduction should be made from the amount of a valuation for liquidated and ascertained damages (see p. 208) because of failure on the contractor's part to complete the Works on time. Even though the PQS knows that the Employer is entitled to such damages, there is no provision in the JCT Conditions of Contract for anyone other than the Employer himself to make the deduction from any sum due to the contractor.

The Employer may, if he so wishes, waive his right to damages, in which case he will make no deduction. It may, however, be prudent for the PQS to remind the architect that damages are due to the Employer – and even how much – so that the architect may be in a position to advise the Employer accordingly.

EXAMPLES OF INTERIM VALUATIONS

The following examples illustrate many of the details which have been discussed earlier in the chapter. They relate to a contract of which particulars are given in Appendix A on pp. 225–30.

Valuation No. 1

This was done on 24 April 1987, approximately one month after the contractor took possession of the site (see Figures 22, 23 and 24). From an initial inspection of the Works, the PQS found that the following work had been done:

About two-thirds of the site clearance work and about 10 per cent of the excavation for the main building; some concrete bases were

SHOPS AND FLATS, THAMES ST., SKINTON

Valuation No. 1 – 24 April 1987		£ p	£ p
Bill No. 1 – Preliminaries			*See below*
Bill No. 2 – Site clearance			3 531 00
Bill No. 3 – Shops and flats			
Excavation	say 10% of £31 174	3 117 00	
Concrete work	27A–27C	3 276 00	
			6 393 00
Bill No. 4 – External works			
Drainage	say 10% of £16 004		1 600 00
			11 524 00
Addition to correct for errors in bills of quantities		2.79%	321 00
			11 845 00
Preliminaries*			
Cost-related items	2.5% of £11 845	296 00	
Time-related items		1 337 00	
Lump sums		2 088 00	3 721 00
			15 566 00
Statutory Bodies			
Thames Water – water main connection		350 00	
Seeboard – electric main connection		350 00	
		700 00	
profit	5%	35 00	
			735 00
Materials on site			
sand	10 tonnes £ 8.14	81 40	
aggregate	20 tonnes £ 7.92	158 40	
cement	12 tonnes £51.04	612 48	
			852 00
			17 153 00
Retention		17 153 00	
less amount subject to nil retention:			
Statutory Bodies		700 00	
	3% of	16 453 00	493 00
	Total of Valuation No. 1		16 660 00

Figure 22

*See p. 174.

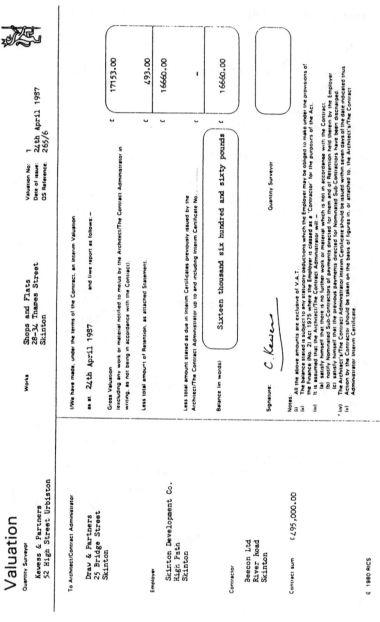

Figure 23

Statement of Retention and of Nominated Sub-Contractors Values

Quantity Surveyor
Kewess & Partners
52 High Street Urbiston

Works Shops and Flats
28-34 Thames Street
Skinton

This Statement relates to :-
Valuation No: 1
Date of issue 24th April 1987
QS Reference 265/6

	Gross Valuation	Amount subject to:			Amount of Retention	Net Valuation	Amount Previously Certified	Balance
		Full Retention of 3 %	Half Retention of 1½%	No Retention				
	£	£	£	£	£	£	£	£
Main Contractor	17 153	16 453	–	700	493	16 660	–	16 660
Nominated Sub-Contractors:-								
TOTAL	17 153	16 453	–	700	493	16 660	–	16 660

No account has been taken of any discounts for cash to which the Contractor may be entitled if discharging the balance within 17 days of the issue of the Architect/S.O.'s Certificate. The sums stated are exclusive of V.A.T.

© 1980 RICS

Figure 24

cast (items 27A–27C in Bill No. 3); about 10 per cent of the drainage work; water and electricity mains connections.

Mess huts, drying sheds, site offices and about half of the temporary fencing erected and temporary water supplies provided; about half of the temporary roads were laid.

Quantities of sand, aggregate and cement stored on site were estimated and noted down.

Commentary on Valuation No. 1

1   As part of the Preliminaries is cost-related, they cannot be calculated until the cost of the builder's work is known. This is indicated by inserting the words 'see below' opposite 'Bill No. 1 – Preliminaries' (Figure 22). See p. 174 for breakdown of Preliminaries.

2   For calculation of the percentage adjustment for errors in the bills of quantities, see p. 63. This item is inserted before the 'Preliminaries' are added because they were excluded when calculating the percentage.

Valuation No. 5

This was carried out on 25 August 1987, by which time five months of the contract period had passed (see Figures 25, 26 and 27). This time the PQS noted that the following work had been done since the job began:

The piling sub-contractors had finished their work and had left the site; excavation was about 80 per cent complete; varying amounts of concrete work and brickwork had been done; woodwork in the roof of the single-storey part was being fixed; some windows, external doors and internal door frames were in position; plumbing and electrical work was in progress; about 45 per cent of the drainage and about 25 per cent of the permanent fencing had been done.

Quantities of sand, aggregate, cement, bricks, partition blocks, timber, felt damp-course and wall ties were stored on site – these were estimated and noted down.

The architect had on 18 August, under clause 35.16, issued a Certificate of Practical Completion of the piling sub-contract.

During the visit, the contractor's surveyor agreed the revised total of £1213 for increased costs of labour and materials, which included the 10 per cent addition under clause 39.8.* Three variation orders had been issued so far but it was agreed that not enough had been done on them to be taken into account in this valuation. The total of Certificates 1–4 inclusive was £99 842.00.

Commentary on Valuation No. 5

1   As part of the Preliminaries is cost-related, they cannot be calculated until the cost of the builder's work is known. This is indicated by inserting the words 'see below' opposite 'Bill No. 1 – Preliminaries' (Figure 25). See p. 174 for breakdown of Preliminaries.

2   For calculation of the percentage adjustment for errors in the bills of quantities, see p. 63. This item is inserted before the 'Preliminaries' are added because they were excluded when calculating the percentage.

3   The lump sums part of Preliminaries is the total of 'Lump Sums (a)' on p. 174.

4   Attendances on the electrical sub-contractor are in proportion to the value of work done on the sub-contract.

5   The amounts subject to half or nil retention are, in the case of nominated sub-contractors and statutory bodies, exclusive of profit and attendance, as those amounts are paid to the main contractor.

6   The deduction for previous payments should be the total of the architect's certificates, not of the PQS's valuations, as it is possible for them to differ.

Valuation No. 12

This was done on 25 March 1988, that is, after twelve months had elapsed (see Figures 28, 29 and 30). Due to bad weather, delays in deliveries because of strikes in the haulage industry during the

* *see* p. 181 and Appendix B, p. 236.

SHOPS AND FLATS, THAMES ST., SKINTON

			£ .p	£ p
Valuation No. 5 – 25 August 1987				
Bill No. 1 – Preliminaries				*See* below
Bill No. 2 – Site clearance				5 531 00
Bill No. 3 – Shops and Flats				
Excavation	say 80% of £31 256		25 004 00	
Concrete work	p. 27	7281		
	28A–28C	3819		
	29F–29H	3265		
	30A–30D	2026		
			16 391 00	
Brickwork	35A–36F	9245		
	37C–37E	1573		
	42A–42D	2181		
			12 999 00	
Woodwork	47E–47H	2926		
	52A–53F	3622		
			6 548 00	
Metalwork	70A–70B	833		
	71A–71D	769		
	73C	209		
			1 811 00	
Plumbing	76A–78N	6167		
	79C–79H	662		
	80A–80B	263		
	84A–86K	1372		
			8 464 00	
Electrical	say 30% of £9389		2 817 00	
Finishings	95C–95L		3 550 00	
Painting	105L		270 00	
				77 854 00
Bill No. 4 – External works				
Drainage	say 45% of £16 004		7 202 00	
Fencing	say 25% of £17 244		4 311 00	
				11 513 00
				94 898 00
Addition to correct for errors in b/q		2.79%		2 647 00
Preliminaries				97 545 00
Cost-related items	2.5% of £97 545		2 438 00	
Time-related items	5 × £1337		6 685 00	
Lump sums			4 177 00	
				13 300 00
	Carried forward			110 845 00

Figure 25

			£ p	£ p
	Brought forward			110 845 00

Nominated sub-contractors

			£ p
Drivas & Co. Ltd – piling			11 340 00
Sparkes & Co. Ltd – electrical			5 000 00
			16 340 00
Profit		5%	817 00
Attendances – piling			720 00
– electrical			250 00

18 127 00

Statutory Bodies

Thames Water – water main connection			350 00
Seeboard – electric main connection			350 00
Segas – gas main connection			500 00
			1 200 00
Profit		5%	60 00

1 260 00

Materials on site

sand	20 tonnes	£ 8.14	162 80
aggregate	30 tonnes	£ 7.92	237 60
cement	6 tonnes	£51.04	306 24
flettons	20 M	£87.60	1752 00
partition blocks	100 m^2	£ 4.78	478 00
dampcourse	20 m^2	£ 0.86	17 20
wall ties	500 no.	£ 3.70	18 50
softwood	200 m	£ 0.69	138 00

		3 110 00
Fluctuations as agreed*		1 213 00
		134 555 00

Retention

		134 555 00
less amounts subject to nil retention:		
Statutory Bodies	1 200	
Fluctuations	1 213	
		2 413 00
		132 142 00
less amount subject to half retention:		
Piling sub-contract		11 340 00
		120 802 00
3% of £120 802 00		3 624 00
1½% of £11 340 00		170 00

3 794 00

Total of Valuation No. 5	130 761 00
Less total of Certificates Nos. 1–4	99 842 00
Total amount due	30 919 00

Figure 25 (*cont.*)

*including 10% addition as clause 39.8

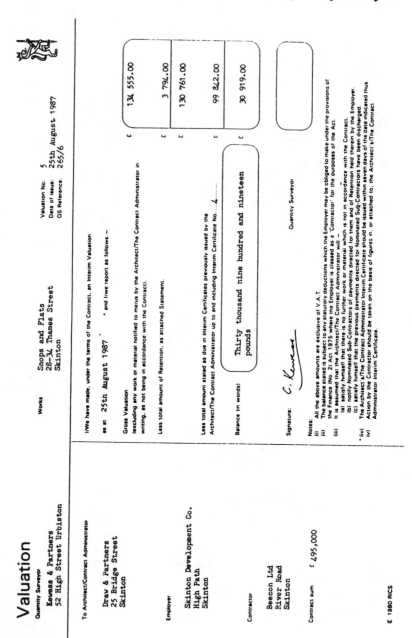

Valuation

Quantity Surveyor
Lewes & Partners
52 High Street Urbiston

Valuation No: 5
Date of issue: 25th August 1987
QS Reference: 265/6

Works   Shops and Flats
               28-34 Thames Street
               Skinton

To Architect/Contract Administrator

Draw & Partners
25 Bridge Street
Skinton

I/We have made, under the terms of the Contract, an Interim Valuation

as at   25th August 1987   ' and I/we report as follows:—

Gross Valuation   £   134 555.00
(excluding any work or material notified to me/us by the Architect/The Contract Administrator in
writing, as not being in accordance with the Contract).

Less total amount of Retention, as attached Statement.   £   3 794.00
                                                                  £   130 761.00

Employer

Skinton Development Co.
High Path
Skinton

Less total amount stated as due in Interim Certificates previously issued by the
Architect/The Contract Administrator up to and including Interim Certificate No.......4.......   £   99 842.00

                                                                  £   30 919.00

Balance (in words)   Thirty thousand nine hundred and nineteen
                        pounds

Signature: *C. Lewes*   Quantity Surveyor

Contractor

Beecon Ltd
River Road
Skinton

Notes:
(i)   All the above amounts are exclusive of V.A.T.
(ii)   The balance stated is subject to any statutory deductions which the Employer may be obliged to make under the provisions of
       the Finance (No. 2) Act 1975 where the Employer is classed as a 'Contractor' for the purposes of the Act.
(iii) It is assumed that the Architect/The Contract Administrator will —
       (a) satisfy himself that there is no further work or material which is not in accordance with the Contract.
       (b) notify Nominated Sub-Contractors of payments directed for them and of Retention held therein by the Employer.
       (c) satisfy himself that the previous payments directed for Nominated Sub-Contractors have been discharged.
(iv)   The Architect's/The Contract Administrator Interim Certificate should be issued within seven days of the date indicated thus
(v)   Action by the Contractor should be taken on the basis of figures in, or attached to, the Architect s/The Contract
       Administrator Interim Certificate.

Contract sum   £ 495,000

© 1980 RICS

Figure 26

Statement of Retention and of Nominated Sub-Contractors Values

Quantity Surveyor
Kevess & Partners
52 High Street Urbiston

Works
Shops and Flats
28-34 Thames Street
Skinton

This Statement relates to :-
Valuation No: 5
Date of issue   25th August 1987
QS Reference   265/6

	Gross Valuation	Amount subject to:			Amount of Retention	Net Valuation	Amount Previously Certified	Balance
		Full Retention of 3 %	Half Retention of 1½ %	No Retention				
	£	£	£	£	£	£	£	£
Main Contractor	118 215	115 802	–	2413	3474	114 741	89 707	25 034
Nominated Sub-Contractors:-								
1. Drivas & Co. Ltd – piling	11 340	–	11 340	–	170	11 170	10 135	1 035
2. Sparkes & Co. Ltd – elec.	5 000	5 000	–	–	150	4 850	–	4 850
TOTAL	134 555	120 802	11 340	2413	3794	130 761	99 842	30 919

No account has been taken of any discounts for cash to which the Contractor may be entitled if discharging the balance within 17 days of the issue of the Architect/S.O.'s Certificate. The sums stated are exclusive of V.A.T.

© 1980 RICS

Figure 27

early part of the year and the delay in installing the lifts, the contract was about five weeks behind schedule.

The six flats on the third floor had been recently completed, those on the second floor were in the early stages of plastering, whilst those on the first floor and the shops on the ground floor were at first fixings stage. Drainage was finished and the fencing was about two-thirds complete. Some external pavings had been laid.

Increased costs of labour and materials had been agreed within the past week at £2364, including 10 per cent addition under clause 39.8. Thirteen variations had been issued to date, one since the last valuation.

On 21 March, by agreement with the contractor, the Employer had taken possession of the six flats on the third floor, although the lifts were not yet in operation. On 22 March, the architect issued a written statement identifying the part taken over and giving the date of possession, as required by clause 18.1 of the JCT Form. The PQS estimated the total value of the six flats to be £80,000 for release of retention purposes.

In January, the architect had agreed to a request to release the retention on the piling sub-contract, and this had been effected in Certificate No. 11.

Just before the February valuation date, it came to light as a result of a complaint from the lifts sub-contractor, that the main contractor had failed to make payment of the sum of £6111 due to the sub-contractor and included in Certificate No. 10. In consequence, work on the lifts installation had stopped and the money had still not been paid. The architect had issued a certificate under clause 35.13.5.2 and the Employer had subsequently made the payment direct, under the provision of clause 35.13.5.3.

During February a claim had been made by the contractor for loss arising under clause 26, due to the architect's failure to provide a schedule of the decorations and details of selected wallpapers required in the flats, thus delaying the completion of the third floor flats. The claim, amounting to £468, was accepted and agreed on 15 March.

The total of Certificates Nos. 1–11 was £247,381.00.

Commentary on Valuation No. 12

1   As part of the Preliminaries is cost-related, they cannot be calculated until the cost of the builder's work is known. This is

indicated by inserting the words 'see below' opposite 'Bill No. 1 – Preliminaries' (Figure 28). See p. 174 for breakdown of Preliminaries.

2 For calculation of the percentage adjustment for errors in the bills of quantities, see p. 63. This item is inserted before the 'Preliminaries' are added because they were excluded when calculating the percentage.

3 The monthly amount of the time-related portion of the Preliminaries has been recalculated to allow for one month's delay.

4 The lump sums part of the Preliminaries is the total of 'lump sums (a)' and 25 per cent of the amounts for 'drying out' and 'cleaning out' in col. (b) in respect of the part handed over on 21 March 1988 (see p. 174).

5 Attendances on nominated sub-contractors are in proportion to the values of work done.

6 The amounts for statutory bodies are the rounded-down sums shown on pp. 89–90, except that, by the valuation date, only the first of the two accounts for rates on temporary buildings had been received from Urbiston Council and only the first four accounts for telephone for the use of the Employer from British Telecom.

7 The amounts subject to half or nil retention are, in the case of nominated sub-contractors and statutory bodies, exclusive of profit and attendance, as those amounts are paid to the main contractor.

8 The total value of the flats handed over on 21 March 1988 estimated at £80 000 must be reduced by a proportion of the value of the piling sub-contract, for which retention has already been released. In later valuations, the total will have to be further reduced by a similar proportion of other nominated sub-contracts released from retention. It is probably best therefore to reduce the total value of the 'relevant part' by the appropriate proportion of the total of all the nominated sub-contracts (except any relating to external works) in all valuations subsequent to the date of handing over. The proportion is:

$$\frac{\text{gross value of the 'relevant part'} \times \text{value of the sub-contract}}{\text{total contract value}}$$

SHOPS AND FLATS, THAMES ST., SKINTON

			£ p	£ p
Valuation No. 12 – 25 March 1988				
Bill No. 1 – Preliminaries				*See* below
Bill No. 2 – Site clearance				5 531 00
Bill No. 3 – Shops and flats				
Excavation	say 90% of £31 256		28 130 00	
Concrete work	p. 27–30	£27 475		
	31A–31E	10 171		
	32C	1 476		
			39 122 00	
Brickwork	p. 34–40	£29 586		
	42A–42F	4 716		
	43A	295		
			34 597 00	
Woodwork	45A–49F	£23 274		
	52A–52J	1 485		
	57A–58F	2 566		
	60A–62C	973		
			28 298 00	
Metalwork	say 75% of £ 9 468		7 101 00	
Plumbing	say 45% of £27 475		12 363 00	
Electrical	say 60% of £ 9 389		5 633 00	
Finishings	say 40% of £22 100		8 840 00	
Glazing	say 25% of			
	98A–101E	3218	804 00	
Painting	103A–103N	766		
	104D–104H	1017		
	105A–106D	2791		
	106L–106P	1254		
			5 828 00	
				170 716 00
Bill No. 4 – External Works				
Drainage	109A–126F		16 004 00	
Fencing	say 60% of £17 244		10 346 00	
Pavings	say 10% of			
	140A–141C		804 00	
				27 154 00
				197 870 00
Addition to correct for errors in b/q			2.79%	5 520 00
			Carried forward	203 390 00

Figure 28

Valuation No. 12 (cont.)

		£ p	£ p
	Brought forward		203 390 00
Preliminaries*			
Cost-related items	2.5% of £203 390	5 084 00	
Time-related items	12 × £1273†	15 276 00	
Lump sums (a)	4 177 00		
(b)	248 00		
		4 425 00	
			24 785 00
Variations	as Valuation No. 11	3 373 00	
	AI No. 62	228 00	3 601 00
Nominated sub-contractors			
Drivas & Co. Ltd	– piling	11 340 00	
Sparkes & Co. Ltd	– electrical	10 700 00	
Asphaltank Ltd	– asphalt work	12 000 00	
Wayward Lifts Ltd	– lifts	6 300 00	
		40 340 00	
Profit	5%	2 017 00	
Attendances	– piling	720	
	– electrical	175	
	– asphalt work	393	
	– lifts	200	
		1 488 00	
			43 845 00
Nominated suppliers:			
Kitchen fitments		1 000 00	
Ironmongery		1 350 00	
Sanitary appliances		2 000 00	
		4 350 00	
Profit	5%	217 00	
			4 567 00
Statutory bodies:			
Thames Water	– water main connection	371 00	
Seeboard	– electric main connection	380 00	
Segas	– gas main connection	549 00	
Urbiston Council	– sewer connections	922 00	
	– rates on temporary bldgs.	1 250 00	
British Telecom	– telephone	326 00	
		3 798 00	
	5%	189 00	3 987 00
Profit	Carried forward		284 175 00

Figure 28 *(cont.)*

---

*see p. 174.

†reduced from £1337 to allow for one month's delay

Valuation No. 12 (cont.)   £ p   £ p

| | | | Brought forward | 284 175 00 |

Materials on site:				
cement	10 tonnes	£51.04	510 00	
fletton bricks	2 M	£87.60	175 00	
partition blocks	80 m²	£ 4.78	382 00	
doors	50 No.	£12.00	600 00	
plumbing goods	say		450 00	

		2 117 00
Fluctuations, as agreed*		2 364 00
Claim under clause 26, as agreed		468 00
		289 124 00

Retention   289 124 00

less amounts subject to nil retention:

Statutory Bodies	3 798	
Piling Sub-cont.	11 340	
Fluctuations	2 364	
Claim	468	
	17 970 00	
	271 154 00	

less amounts subject to half retention:

Flats handed over 21/3/88:

	80 000	
less proportion of piling s/c	1 832	78 168 00
		192 986 00

3% of £192 986 00	5 789 00
1½% of £78 168 00	1 172 00
	6 961 00

Total of Valuation No. 12	282 163 00
Less total of Certificates Nos. 1–11	247 381 00
Total amount due	34 782 00

*including 10% addition as Clause 39.8

Figure 28 (*cont.*)

Valuation

Quantity Surveyor
Kevess & Partners
52 High Street Urbiston

Works	Shops and Flats
	28-34 Thames Street
	Skinton

Valuation No:	12
Date of issue:	25th March 1988
QS Reference:	265/6

To Architect/Contract Administrator

Draw & Partners
25 Bridge Street
Skinton

I/We have made, under the terms of the Contract, an interim Valuation

as at 25th March 1988   and I/we report as follows:—

Gross Valuation
(excluding any work or material notified to me/us by the Architect/The Contract Administrator in writing, as not being in accordance with the Contract).

£ 289 124.00

Less total amount of Retention, as attached Statement.

£ 6 961.00

£ 282 163.00

Employer

Skinton Development Co.
High Path
Skinton

Less total amount stated as due in Interim Certificates previously issued by the Architect/The Contract Administrator up to and including Interim Certificate No. ...11......

£ 247 381.00

Balance (in words)   Thirty-four thousand seven hundred and eighty-two pounds

£ 34 782.00

Contractor

Beecon Ltd
River Road
Skinton

Signature: C. Kevess   Quantity Surveyor

Contract sum   £ 495,000.00

Notes:
(i)   All the above amounts are exclusive of V.A.T.
(ii)   The balance stated is subject to any statutory deductions which the Employer may be obliged to make under the provisions of the Finance (No. 2) Act 1975 where the Employer is classed as a 'Contractor' for the purposes of the Act.
(iii)   It is assumed that the Architect/The Contract Administrator will:—
    (a) satisfy himself that there is no further work or material which is not in accordance with the Contract.
    (b) notify Nominated Sub-Contractors of payments directed for them and of Retention held therein by the Employer.
    (c) satisfy himself that the previous payments directed for Nominated Sub-Contractors have been discharged.
*(iv)   The Architect's/The Contract Administrator's Interim Certificate should be issued within seven days of the date indicated thus
(v)   Action by the Contractor should be taken on the basis of figures in, or attached to, the Architect's/The Contract Administrator Interim Certificate.

© 1980 RICS

Figure 29

Statement of Retention and of Nominated Sub-Contractors Values

Quantity Surveyor
Kewss & Partners
52 High Street Urbiston

Works
Shops and Flats
28–34 Thames Street
Skinton

This Statement relates to :-
Valuation No: 12
Date of issue   25th March 1988
QS Reference   265/6

	Gross Valuation	Amount subject to:			Amount of Retention	Net Valuation	Amount Previously Certified	Balance
		Full Retention of 3 %	Half Retention of 1½ %	No Retention				
	£	£	£	£	£	£	£	£
Main Contractor	248 784	163 987	78 168	6 629	6091	242 693	214 022	28 671
Nominated Sub-Contractors:-								
1. Drivas & Co. Ltd – piling	11 340			11 340	–	11 340	11 340	–
2. Sparkes & Co. Ltd – elec.	10 700	10 700	–	–	321	10 379	6 887	3 492
3. Asphaltank Ltd – asphalt work	12 000	12 000	–	–	360	11 640	9 021	2 619
4. Wayward Lifts – lifts	6 300	6 300	–	–	189	6 111	6 111	–
TOTAL	289 124	192 987	78 168	17 969	6961	282 163	247 381	34 782

No account has been taken of any discounts for cash to which the Contractor may be entitled if discharging the balance within 17 days of the issue of the Architect/S.O.'s Certificate. The sums stated are exclusive of V.A.T.

© 1980 RICS

Figure 30

In this case the calculation of the reduction in relation to the piling sub-contract only is $\dfrac{80\ 000 \times 11\ 340}{495\ 000} = \pounds 1832.$

9 The deduction for previous payments should be the total of the architect's certificates, not of the PQS's valuations, as it is possible for them to differ.

10 No deduction should be made of the amount paid direct by the Employer to Wayward Lifts (see p. 194), nor for any liquidated damages which may be due because of the five weeks' delay. However, the PQS should draw the architect's attention to such deductions so that he may remind the Employer of his right to deduct from the payment stated in the certificate as due.

REFERENCES

1. *Standard Form of Building Contract, 1980 Edition*, clause 30.2.
2. TURNER, DENNIS F., *Quantity Surveying Practice and Administration* (London: George Godwin Ltd, 1983), p. 159.
3. *Standard Form of Building Contract, 1980 Edition*, Articles of Agreement, Second Recital.
4. The Query Sheet, *Chartered Surveyor, BQS Quarterly*, Vol. 1, No. 2, December 1973, p. 40.
5. TURNER, DENNIS F., *Quantity Surveying Practice and Administration* (London: George Godwin Ltd, 1983), p. 164.
6. GOODACRE, P. E., *Formula Method of Price Adjustment for Building Contracts* (Reading: College of Estate Management, 1978), p. 96, Q. 2.
7. *Standard Form of Building Contract, 1980 Edition*, clause 36.4.4.
8. ibid., clause 36.3.1.

13

Final accounts

In order to be able to make final payment to a contractor of the sum to which he is entitled under the terms of the contract, it is usually necessary to produce a final account. In any but the very smallest jobs, there will be many adjustments to be made to the Contract Sum and a detailed document is necessary to show, to the satisfaction of all concerned, what amount of money the Employer is liable to pay and the contractor is entitled to receive and how it has been calculated.

In the case of lump sum contracts, therefore, the final account begins with the Contract Sum, shows what amounts are deducted and what amounts are added (and for what reasons) and ends with the adjusted total sum. This sum, when agreed by the contractor, is the total amount which the Employer will pay to the contractor for the work he has done.

In the case of measured contracts, the final account is built up from nil to an 'ascertained final sum', which is the aggregate of amounts for named parts of the project. The ascertained final sum is the total amount which the Employer will pay to the contractor.

The responsibility for preparing the final account is that of the PQS and the JCT Form limits the time in which the task should be completed. As previously stated (see p. 103), the PQS has a duty to endeavour to complete the variation accounts within the period stated in clause 30.6.1, and the whole account in time for the architect to issue the Final Certificate at the time specified in clause 30.8.

It will be necessary for the PQS to obtain the contractor's agreement to the total of the account. To be able to give this, the contractor will need to see the supporting details. Accordingly, a photocopy of the whole document, fully priced and totalled, should be sent to him, either complete or in sections as they are finished. As there will often be some points of disagreement, the PQS and the contractor's surveyor will need to meet and discuss those points, negotiate revisions to any suggested item rates and prices, etc., until eventually the whole is agreed. Each of them (or their principals) will then sign the summary page to signify their agreement.

CONSTITUENTS OF FINAL ACCOUNTS

Lump sum contracts (except those based on bills of approximate quantities)

The final account will usually consist of a document which contains most or all of the following sections, although not necessarily in the order given:

(a) a summary of the account;
(b) adjustments of prime cost sums;
(c) adjustments of provisional sums;
(d) variation accounts;
(e) adjustment of provisional items;
(f) claims;
(g) fluctuations in costs of labour, materials and statutory contributions, levies, and taxes.

The document may be handwritten or it may be typed, depending on the client's requirements. As multiple copies are not usually needed, the expense of typing seems unjustified. The client is often only concerned with the summary and, if that is so, that is all that needs to be typed. A photocopy of the handwritten document will provide a copy for the contractor's perusal and agreement as suggested above.

The foregoing list of sections of the account require comment as follows.

Summary of the account

The summary usually consists of a single page of double billing paper showing the contract sum, the respective total deduction and addition amounts transferred from each of the succeeding sections, and the final total. At the bottom of the page will appear the signatures of the contractor and PQS. A suitable format is shown in Figure 31.

Adjustments of prime cost sums

The summary of the adjustments forms the first page of the section, the following pages showing complete details of the deductions and additions respectively of the p.c. sums and the actual costs, with the profit amounts. Figures 10 and 11 show alternative formats for the summary. Figure 10 illustrates a method of setting out the supporting details.

Adjustments of provisional sums

This section will be similar in layout to the preceding one, except that there will be no separate profit amounts. The additions items set against each provisional sum will normally be measured and priced in exactly the same way as those in variation accounts, being for work carried out by the general contractor in the majority of cases.

Variation accounts

The variation accounts (see p. 103) may commence with a summary showing the total of deductions and the total of additions for each separate variation or, alternatively, the nett total saving or extra for each. Following the summary, the supporting details are given consisting of measured items grouped as omissions and additions under each AI. A third format shows only the total nett saving or extra for all the variations together, and the presentation of the details is in the form of a bill of omissions and a bill of additions without items being separated under each variation.

Adjustment of provisional items

This section of final accounts requires more detailed consideration as, unlike the other sections, it does not form a separate chapter.

When the quantity of an item or group of items of work cannot be accurately ascertained at the time of preparing the tender documents, the item or group of items is distinguished by being described as 'provisional'. In the case of single items, it will appear in brackets at the end of the description. In the case of a group of items, for example, those for the substructure of a building, the words 'The following "All Provisional" ' will normally precede the group.

In all cases, whether single items or groups of items, it is incumbent upon the PQS to deduct the value of the provisional items from the contract sum and to substitute the value of measured items as actually carried out. This procedure is required by clauses 30.6.2.2 and 30.6.2.12 of the JCT Form. Even where the quantity of an item as executed is the same as that in the bills, the deduction and addition should still be shown. Otherwise, it may be supposed that the provisional item has been overlooked. The value of the remeasured items will be ascertained in the same way as in the case of variations (see pp. 104–6).

The advantage of giving measured items in the bills even though the quantities are not accurate, rather than allowing a provisional sum instead, is first, that unit rates are then available for use in valuing the work as remeasured. Secondly, the contractor is given a much more definite picture of the scope and nature of the work than he would otherwise have.

Claims

Claims for additional payments which have been accepted under clauses 26.1 and 34.3 of the JCT Form should each be fully and separately set out, detailing the calculations of the agreed sums. If the section is large enough to warrant it, a summary of the claims should be presented on its first page.

Fluctuations in costs of labour and materials, etc.

This is a particular form of claim arising under clauses 38, 39 and 40 of the JCT Form. The details should be fully set out to show how the amount of the claim has been calculated (see Chapters 9 and 10).

Measured contracts (that is, those based upon bills of approximate quantities or schedules of rates.)

The final account for contracts which require the complete measurement of the Works will usually be a simpler, though more lengthy document. As there is no contract sum, the account will not be an adjustment account (i.e. showing deductions and additions), but will consist wholly of additions amounts.

Clause 30.6.2 of the JCT Form for use with bills of approximate quantities lists the components of the 'Ascertained Final Sum' and they may be conveniently grouped together as follows. The same groupings may also be applied to schedule of rates contracts, as appropriate.

Summary of the account

The summary cannot commence with a contract sum as there is none, nor in consequence can it show any omissions. Instead, it will give a list of the succeeding sections with a total sum against each.

Bills of remeasurement

These will be similar in format to the measured sections of bills of quantities prepared for tendering purposes.

Preliminaries

This section will consist of the appropriate preliminaries items, valued in accordance with the Conditions of the contract.

Nominated subcontractors', nominated suppliers', and statutory bodies' accounts

This section will be similar to the 'adjustment of p.c. sums' section of the account for a lump sum contract, but without the omissions amounts.

Claims

This section will be similar to that in an account for a lump sum contract (see under 'Claims', p. 205).

Fluctuations

This section will also be similar to that in an account for a lump sum contract (see under 'Fluctuations in costs of labour and materials', p. 205).

Prime cost contracts

The final account for prime cost contracts is in essence a very simple document. It shows the total of each of the constituents of the prime cost, i.e. labour, plant, and materials, and in addition, either the fixed fee or the calculation of the fee where it is a percentage of the prime cost. If there is a target cost (see pp. 19–20), the resulting addition or deduction should also be shown. In the event of a situation arising being such as to warrant an adjustment of the fee,* details of the calculation of the adjustment should also be given.

FINAL CERTIFICATE

When the final account has been agreed, a photocopy of the original document (or, if sufficient, just the summary pages) will be sent to the architect or the client (if appropriate) with a notification of the balance due to the contractor in settlement, after deduction of the total amount of interim certificates. It may be necessary to prepare a separate statement to show the reduced sum due, if the Employer has made payments when the contractor has defaulted. Examples are: where the contractor has failed to pay insurance premiums (clauses 21 and 22A of the JCT Form) and where the contractor has failed to pay nominated sub-contractors the sums included in interim certificates (clause 35.13). (It should be noted that the Form does not require such amounts to be deducted from the contract sum, i.e. in the final account, but to be deducted by the Employer from 'any sums due or to become due to the contractor'.)

Upon notification of the sum due, the architect is required to issue his Final Certificate within two months after the happening of the last of the events listed in clause 30.8. This should state (*a*) the adjusted contract sum or the ascertained final sum (i.e. the

---

*See clause 26(1) of Fixed Fee Form of Prime Cost Contract.

total of the final account), (*b*) the total of amounts paid on account and (*c*) the difference between the two amounts expressed as a balance due from one party to the other. Such balance is stated to be 'subject to any deductions authorized by the Conditions', such as those instanced in the preceding paragraph.

LIQUIDATED AND ASCERTAINED DAMAGES

Clause 24.2 of the JCT Form provides for liquidated damages to be paid or allowed by the contractor to the Employer calculated at the rate stated in the Appendix to the Conditions, when a contract exceeds the contract period or, if an extension has been granted, the extended contract period.

Clause 24.2 says that the Employer may deduct any sum for liquidated damages from 'any monies due or to become due to the contractor'. As far as the PQS is concerned, therefore, the deduction of any amount for liquidated damages due, should be made by the Employer from the sum stated in a certificate issued by the architect, as due to the contractor. All that the PQS should do is to notify the architect of the amount of liquidated damages payable, so that the architect may in turn inform the Employer of the amount which he is entitled to deduct, if he so wishes. The PQS should not deduct liquidated damages in the final account.

EXAMPLE OF FINAL ACCOUNT

Figure 31 shows a method of setting out the summary of the final account for the contract detailed in Appendix A. The supporting details relate to the examples given in Chapters 7–9.

SHOPS AND FLATS, THAMES ST., SKINTON

for

SKINTON DEVELOPMENT CO.

FINAL ACCOUNT

	Omissions £ p	Additions £ p
Contract sum as contract dated 23rd February 1987		495 000 00
Adjustment of prime cost and provisional sums	8 486 34	
Variations		6 167 30
Remeasurement of provisional work	849 09	
Fluctuations in costs of labour and materials		5 157 61
Claim for loss under clause 26		468 00
	9 335 43	506 792 91
Less omissions		9 335 43
TOTAL OF FINAL ACCOUNT		497 457 48

Signed for and on behalf of

    Beecon Ltd,
    River Road,
    Skinton,
    Middlesex.

Signed for and on behalf of

    Kewess & Partners
    52, High Street,
    Urbiston,
    Surrey.

....

15 June 1989

....

Figure 31 Final account summary

14

Cost control

THE QUANTITY SURVEYOR'S ROLE

Cost control has been defined as 'the controlling measures necessary to ensure that the authorized cost of the project is not exceeded'.[1] Initially, the 'authorized cost' is the contract sum but at subsequent times in the construction period, it will need to be adjusted to take account of necessary savings and of additional costs which the Employer is willing and able to meet.

The 'controlling measures' are usually in the hands of the Employer and his architect. The PQS is not normally in a position to exercise control of cost himself unless, as is sometimes the case, he has been appointed project manager, when he has overall control of the project. His usual role, however, is that of adviser to those who have that control and so is one of monitoring and reporting on costs rather than controlling them.

The contractor's quantity surveyor likewise is unlikely to have any direct control of the costs of construction but is in the position of monitoring costs and expenditure and advising the contracts manager on such matters as the value of work done to date and the likely eventual total value of the contract. The contracts manager will be concerned with the relationship between the contractor's expenditure on the construction work and the total of payments received or anticipated from the Employer. While the payments are in excess of the expenditure, there is a profit. If in any part of the work, however, the contractor's costs exceed the amounts payable under the contract terms, there will exist a loss situation, at least so far as that section of the work is concerned. The contractor's quantity surveyor will be expected to be able to explain why this situation has arisen and may even be expected to foresee a potential loss-making position developing and to warn the contracts manager so that he may take what steps are necessary to minimize or reverse the loss.

Such a position may arise from any one or more of the following causes:

(a) inefficient deployment of resources (labour, plant, and materials);

(b) excessive wastage or theft of materials;

(c) plant being allowed to stand idle or under-utilized;

(d) adverse weather or working conditions;

(e) delays arising from one or more of a variety of causes;

(f) under-pricing of tender documents by assumptions in regard to labour times, types and sizes of plant, etc., which do not equate with the realities of the construction work.

Recovery of additional expenditure under some of the foregoing heads may be possible (e.g. items (c), (d) and (e) on the list) by successful claims within the provisions of the contract but this will not be so in all cases.

Cost control from the viewpoint of the contractor's quantity surveyor, therefore, is distinct from that of the PQS. Although the concern of both of them centres around the total value of a project, the former is concerned with the relationship between the contractor's expenditure and payments to him by the Employer, while the latter is concerned with the relationship between the total amount that the Employer is willing and able to spend and the total sum that he is liable to pay under the terms of the contract.

In order to provide a basis for controlling cost, there must be a contract sum or an estimated value of the initial contract. In the case of lump sum contracts, there will be a contract sum but in the case of prime cost and schedule of rates contracts there will not and it will be necessary for the PQS to prepare an estimate of contract value, preferably in the form of a cost plan. This will provide the basis for the necessary control mechanism, if cost is to be controlled at all.

MONITORING AND REPORTING ON THE FINANCIAL POSITION

The Employer will need to be kept informed by the PQS of the financial position of the contract. This is so that he will be able to make the necessary arrangements to have the finance available to pay the contractor within the stipulated time upon presentation of interim certificates and also so that he may be warned of any possibility or likelihood of the 'authorized cost' of the project being exceeded. He may then take steps, as considered appropriate, to increase his borrowing capacity or to effect savings on the project to ensure that the final cost is within his budget limit.

There are thus two aspects to financial reports: (a) the current position and (b) the likely total cost. In order to carry out his duties adequately, the PQS will have to take account of all the actual or likely causes of adjustment to the contract sum (as far as he is able to do so), as follows:

(a) expenditure of p.c. sums;
(b) expenditure of provisional sums;
(c) variations;
(d) claims;
(e) recoverable fluctuations in costs.

Expenditure of p.c. sums

The position at any time with regard to the expenditure of p.c. sums will usually be clear cut. The architect either will or will not have issued instructions to the contractor on each of the p.c. sums and, where he has, the amount of the saving or extra will be known. Where he has not taken a decision, then no adjustment of the p.c. sum can be made, unless it is obvious that it is going to be exceeded. In that case, the PQS should include in his financial statement an estimated addition to that p.c. sum. The consequent effect (if any) on the amounts for profit and attendances in relation to each p.c. sum will also be known to the same extent.

Expenditure on provisional sums

Where provisional sums are to cover the cost of such matters as telephone calls made on behalf of the Employer or general rates payable to local authorities on temporary buildings, then estimates of the likely expenditure will have to be included if actual costs are not known. Where provisional sums are to cover work to be carried out by the general contractor, the actual cost of the work (if already carried out and measured and valued) should be substituted for the respective provisional sums. If the work has not yet been measured and valued, then an estimate of the likely cost should be made and substituted for the provisional sums. Such estimates will usually be done by the 'approximate quantities' method, i.e. by measuring the main items of work involved reasonably accurately (but not necessarily exactly). The measured items are then priced at 'all-in' rates, i.e. at rates (based on bill rates where possible) which allow not only for all the work described in each item but also for the cost of all related items which have not been separately measured.

Variations

Where variations have been included in Architect's Instructions and have been accurately measured and valued, the nett extra cost or saving (i.e. taking both additions and omissions into account) should be incorporated in the financial assessment. In regard to those variations which have not been measured and valued, including any which are expected but have not yet been ordered by the architect, the total nett value of each should be estimated in the manner described under 'Expenditure on provisional sums' and be taken into account.

Claims

If claims can be dealt with promptly, the amounts allowed can be taken into account when the next financial statement is made. Claims which have been presented but are still outstanding should be valued as accurately as reasonably possible (erring, if anything, on the generous side) and included in the statement. If any claim is subsequently rejected, it will, of course, be omitted from the next statement. Any claims unlikely to be accepted can probably be safely ignored.

Fluctuations

Fluctuations which are recoverable under the terms of the contract should be valued at least monthly for inclusion in interim valuations. Where the NEDO Formula Method is used, fluctuations will be calculated at each valuation date anyway (see p. 142).

The amounts so agreed will be included in financial reports and an estimate of future payments will need to be made for the purpose of forecasting the likely total cost of the project.

It may be thought that interim valuations are, in effect, reports on the current financial position of a project. While to a large extent this is so, they do not necessarily give a complete picture. They give the accurate current position of expenditure by the Employer but they do not necessarily include all known costs for which he is currently liable. The position is also clouded to some extent by the retention, particularly where there have been some releases, and also by the inclusion in valuations of the value of unfixed materials. Examples are given below of expenditure to which the Employer is committed but which may not be included in the latest interim valuation, often because of time lag. The value of unfixed materials, included in interim valuations, would be excluded from financial reports.

(*a*) work covered by p.c. sums which has not yet been completed or of which the value has not yet been included in an interim valuation;

(*b*) work which is covered by provisional sums or which is the subject of variation orders, which is still in progress but was insufficiently advanced for inclusion in the last valuation;

(*c*) fluctuations for which the Employer is liable but for which supporting details are awaited from the contractor;

(*d*) claims which are expected to be accepted but which have not yet been settled.

The contractor's quantity surveyor will be involved in preparing similar financial reports for the contracts manager, contracts director or managing director. His reports will, of course, be similar in most respects to those prepared by the PQS. They may differ, however, in the following matters.

(*a*) Variations may be included which the contractor claims have been ordered but which have not been confirmed in writing. These may or may not be confirmed later (see p. 100).

(*b*) The value of all claims will be included, whether accepted or not. A distinction may be shown, however, between those agreed or likely to be agreed and those unlikely to be accepted.

(*c*) The valuation of variations, remeasured work, claims and fluctuations will differ, partly because of item rates and prices which remain to be agreed and partly because aspects of claims and fluctuations payments may be the subject of dispute.

Examples of financial reports are given in Figures 32 and 33.

As the effective control of cost lies with the architect, it is desirable that the PQS should bring his influence to bear to encourage the exercise of that control. He can do so by providing cost reports on the current and future financial positions, which are prompt, reliable and up-to-date. It is also desirable that, before issuing instructions that affect the cost of the contract, the architect should consult the PQS on the likely effect and obtain advice on the cost of any alternative that may be available.

FORECASTING CLIENT'S CAPITAL EXPENDITURE FLOW

If a contract is large with a cost of millions of pounds to be expended over several years, it is essential to make a reasonably reliable forecast of the likely flow of expenditure. Even where costs are more modest, and contract time correspondingly shorter, it is to a client's advantage to be able to anticipate his cash flow requirement and to be able to arrange for finance to be available accordingly.

In consequence, it is often part of the PQS's task to prepare, either in tabular or graphical form, an anticipated 'rate of spend' or 'expenditure flow' forecast.

In order to do this, it is necessary to prepare a programme for the carrying out of the various parts of the construction work. A progress chart or 'bar chart', as illustrated in Figure 34, is commonly used to show such a programme. If the contractor has produced a programme which he has submitted to the architect or project manager or if he is willing to make his programme available to the PQS, so much the better. Using bill rates and prices (or schedule rates and prices, if there is no bill), each section of the work is valued, the totals being broken down into monthly amounts over the period allocated to each section, as shown in Figure 34. The monthly amounts are then totalled and to each total is added the appropriate proportion of the Preliminaries. The final totals for each month (which together should equal the contract sum) can then be tabulated or plotted on a graph.

A graph plotted from such data is usually referred to as an 'S-

SHOPS & FLATS, 28–34 THAMES ST., SKINTON

FINANCIAL REPORT NO. 10

Current position as at 2 April 1988

	£
Value of measured work as bills of quantities as at 25 March 1988	203 390
Value of Preliminaries as at 25 March 1988	24 785
Payments to nominated subcontractors plus profit and attendances as Valuation No. 12	43 845
Payments to nominated suppliers plus profit as Valuation No. 12	4 567
Payments to Statutory Bodies plus profit as Valuation No. 12	3 987
Variations	3 601
Fluctuations in labour and materials costs	2 363
Claim under clause 26, as agreed	468
Claim under clause 26 outstanding but for which liable	2 500
VALUE OF WORK CARRIED OUT TO DATE	289 506
Total actual expenditure as Certificate No. 12 (before deduction of retention)	289 124
Total anticipated expenditure to date as forecast*	341 223

5 April 1988

Figure 32   Example of report on current financial position of a contract

*see p. 221.

SHOPS & FLATS, 28–34 THAMES ST., SKINTON

FINANCIAL REPORT NO. 11

Estimated Total Cost

	£
Contract sum	495 000
Less Contingency sum	8 000
	487 000
Less Prime cost and provisional sums (nett omission)	8 486*
	478 514
Variations	6 000
Fluctuations in labour and materials costs	5 000
Claims	2 968
	492 482
Contingency sum for remainder of contract	3 500
ESTIMATED TOTAL COST OF CONTRACT	495 982

5 April 1988

Figure 33 Example of report on likely total cost of a contract

*Wayward Lifts' increased costs claim not received at date of preparation of this report (*see* p. 85–6).

CONTRACT PROGRAMME CHART (Simplified)*

Operation	1	2	3	4	5	6	7	8	9	10	11	12	13	14	15	16	17	18	19	20	Totals
Site clearance	3 685	2 000																			5 685
Excavation	2 432	4 325	5 141	3 458	3 271	6 916	6 586														32 129
Piling Nom. S/C.		5 400	5 400	2 205																	13 005
Mains services connections	756				567	945															2 268
Drainage					3 458	3 551	1 962	1 683	1 683	1 870	934	863									16 004
Concrete work	843	3 728	4 738	4 739	1 789	3 911	4 673	5 609	5 981	5 047	5 178	4 234	5 538								56 008
Asphalt tanking and roofing Nom. S/C.		1 440	3 420					6 796	3 654	2 160											17 460
Brickwork and blockwork			1 870	7 477	5 981	5 648	5 567	6 543	6 796	6 802											46 684
Woodwork				2 992	1 940	3 668	3 739	5 700	5 449	7 041	3 681	7 989	7 225	7 225	8 075	5 690	5 152	1 222			63 502
Metalwork									556	1 295	925	483									9 733
Plumbing and heating				1 589	371				3 176	2 061	3 176	4 255	2 535	2 589	3 969	5 558	1 167				32 777
Plastering and tiling				1 573	2 702	2 405	2 461	1 517	1 341	1 341	1 714	2 774	2 774	1 070							22 717
Lifts Nom. S/C.												10 800	9 000	9 000	5 400	2 790					36 990
Electrical work Nom. S/C.									1 800	7 236	7 560			2 430	3 384	3 179	3 863				29 452
Glazing								1 664	1 017	1 295	556				1 851	1 133	1 386				8 626
Painting and decorating									1 480	1 480	1 666	1 388	1 388	1 388	1 388	1 388	1 388	1 110	1 110	630	17 746
Fencing					3 701	278		2 312	1 065								1 497	4 625	1 849		17 244
External pavings							1 851											998	1 953	1 288	8 440
Provisional sums	137	138	137	138	137	138	137	138	138	138	137	1 497	998	1 497	137	138	137	138	1 237	138	5 000
Preliminaries	2 730	3 580	3 251	2 012	1 727	1 722	1 792	1 910	1 282	1 865	1 724	1 190	1 452	1 669	1 669	1 734	2 010	2 897	1 944	2 900	41 480
Dayworks and contingencies	602	603	602	603	602	603	602	603	603	603	602	603	602	603	603	603	602	603	602	603	12 050
Totals	11 185	21 214	24 559	26 786	28 651	31 636	32 628	33 892	34 402	31 571	31 213	31 906	32 413	29 737	26 695	22 213	17 202	12 981	8 695	5 421	495 000

Notes: Adjustment for errors in bills of quantities distributed over monthly values.
　　　 Dayworks and contingencies have been included so that the total agrees with the Contract Sum.

*The programme chart relates to the contract described in Appendix A, page 225

Figure 34   Use of programme chart for expenditure forecasting

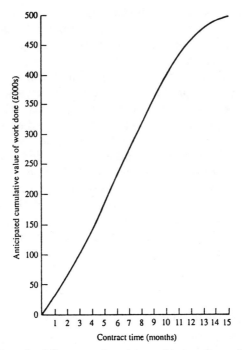

Figure 35 Standard S-curve of anticipated 'rate of spend'

curve' graph because of the shape of the graph. It indicates a build-up in the rate of expenditure over the first two or three months, an acceleration of the rate over the main part of the contract period and a gradual run-down over the final three months or so. Figure 35 shows a typical S-curve graph for a £500 000 contract over a fifteen-month contract period.

A graph produced as described above will, of course, indicate anticipated cumulative monthly total values of work done and not a forecast rate of client's expenditure. The difference between the two is the amount of retention deductible during the contract period and the amounts of releases of retention at its end. From the amounts of monthly values of work should be deducted the proportion of value to be retained, and amounts of releases should be added. The latter may be only at the end of the contract period or may be earlier in the case of sectional completion. The adjusted amounts may then be plotted to give an S-curve showing expected rate of expenditure by the client.

There is an alternative method of producing such a graph. If the totals of interim valuations for a number of contracts are plotted and curves of 'best fit' are drawn an S-curve of approximately the same shape will result for each contract. It follows, therefore, that it is possible, within a given range of cost and over a limited range of contract times, to produce a 'standard' S-curve which can be used to predict expenditure flows for further contracts without the need to go through the detailed procedure described above.

A third method of producing an S-curve graph of value of work executed is by the use of a formula. This method is used by the Department of Health and by the Property Services Agency.[2] It is really a development from the method described in the last paragraph because, having produced standard S-curves in the manner described, the Department then proceeded to determine the underlying mathematical formula. The formula devised and used by the Department is

$$y = S[x + Cx^2 - Cx - \frac{1}{K}(6x^3 - 9x^2 + 3x)]$$

where y = cumulative value of work executed in £

S = contract sum in £

x = proportion of contract time completed

C and K = parameters relating to contract value:

contract value £s	C	K
10,000– 50,000	–0.439	5.464
50,000–100,000	–0.370	4.880
100,000–200,000	–0.295	4.360
200,000–500,000	–0.220	3.941
500,000–2m	–0.145	3.595
2m–3½m	0.010	4.000
3½m–5½m	0.110	3.980
5½m–7½m	0.159	3.780
7½m–9m	0.056	3.323
over 9m	–0.028	3.090

It will be obvious that the formula has to be used for each month's anticipated value of work done – which means fifteen times for a fifteen-month contract, etc. The mathematical work entailed presents no great problem when a computer (or programmable calculator) is available but without one, the volume and tedium of the necessary calculations may deter many surveyors from using this method.

It is important, of course, that having produced a forecast of rate of expenditure, the information should be given to the client, either direct or through the architect, so that he may use it to arrange finance for the project. It may be necessary on large jobs to revise the forecast rate of expenditure at any point during the contract period for the remaining period, in the light of actual expenditure and if this is done, again, the client should be given the revised information without delay.

A further use of the S-curve graph is to plot the totals of interim valuations as they are done, thus producing a curve of actual expenditure. If the latter is seen to be beginning to fall short of the anticipated expenditure, it will provide early warning of possible trouble. There may be a satisfactory explanation, such as a prolonged period of bad weather or a strike in the construction industry or in a related industry. If there is no obvious explanation, there may be an indication that the contractor is running into difficulties, financial or otherwise. The early warning may provide an opportunity to remedy the situation.

In such circumstances as those described in the last paragraph, the formula can be used (*a*) to determine a revised completion date (*b*) to forecast likely expenditure in future months, based on actual expenditure in past months, and (*c*) to calculate the rate of expenditure necessary to achieve completion by the original date stated in the contract[3] (although experience has shown that this is seldom possible).

Figure 36 shows a graph of anticipated and actual expenditure for the contract of which particulars are given in Appendix A. All values shown are those before deduction of retention. Anticipated expenditure has been calculated using the DHSS formula, using values $C = -0.220$ and $K = +3.941$. The calculated forecast of cumulative expenditure for each month is as follows:

Month	Expenditure	Month	Expenditure
1	£ 13 814	11	£308 529
2	£ 32 170	12	£341 223
3	£ 54 505	13	£372 242
4	£ 80 250	14	£401 021
5	£108 843	15	£426 994
6	£139 717	16	£449 598
7	£172 307	17	£468 265
8	£206 045	18	£482 431
9	£240 376	19	£491 531
10	£274 725	20	£495 000

The curve of actual expenditure shows monthly values before deduction of retention and exclusive of materials on site, fluctuations and claims, thus allowing an undistorted comparison to be made. It will be seen that the expenditure during the first nine months was higher than forecast, but after that it dropped markedly below the forecast level. The reasons for this were: bad weather, the shut-down for Christmas 1987 and the New Year and the subsequent cessation of work on the lifts installation (see p. 194). From March onwards, the rate of production increased and by July, actual expenditure had almost caught up with the forecast value.

By plotting actual expenditure each month, it was possible to see at the December valuation that the curve was flattening out, thus giving warning of possible problems ahead. In fact, the causes were identified, as noted above, and steps were taken to remedy the situation so that the contract was eventually completed on time.

FORECASTING CONTRACTOR'S EARNINGS AND EXPENDITURE

The same information as is produced by the forecasting techniques described above, is of value to the contractor. It enables him to monitor the financial progress of each of the contracts running at any time. The S-curve of anticipated cumulative values of work done represents to the contractor his anticipated or 'programmed' earnings. The rate of client's expenditure becomes, from his point of view, actual earnings.[4] A comparison between the two provides an indication whether the financial progress of the contract is satisfactory or not.

Similarly, a comparison may be made between earnings and expenditure and a graph plotted each month showing cumulative values will indicate clearly whether a contract is making a profit or a loss. If it is desired to establish more specifically where a profit or a loss is being made, the earnings may be broken down approximately into its components for ready comparison with expenditure. Gobourne gives an example of such a comparison on p. 9 of the reference last quoted.

The value of such comparisons, if carried out at least once a month, is that they enable the contractor to have early warning of

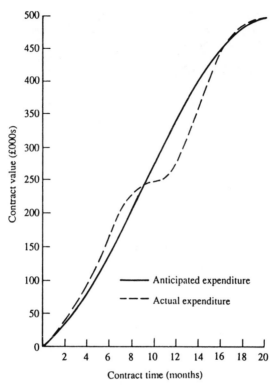

Figure 36 S-curve of anticipated and actual expenditure (before deduction of retention)

a loss-making situation before the position becomes irretrievable. By pin-pointing where the losses are being made, the contractor can take action to remedy the situation. Again, prompt and up-to-date information is the key to practical use of financial analysis. Otherwise, its value is merely historical. Thus, the contractor's quantity surveyor who keeps the contracts manager regularly and accurately informed on the current relationship between earnings and expenditure, is of considerable value to his employer.

REFERENCES

1. AQUA GROUP, *Contract Administration for Architects and Quantity Surveyors*, 7th Ed., (London: Collins, 1986), p. 14.
2. HUDSON, K. W., DHSS expenditure forecasting method, *Chartered Surveyor, BQS Quarterly*, Vol. 5, No. 3, Spring 1978, p. 42

3. COST INTELLIGENCE SERVICE, DHSS, *Health Notice HN(78)149 Forecasting Incidences of Expenditure*, reference CON/C462/17, November 1978, pp. 2–3.
4. GOBOURNE, J., *Cost Control in the Construction Industry* (London: Butterworth & Co. Ltd, 1973), pp. 7–8.

Appendix A

Particulars of contract referred to in the examples given in the text.

Location of site:	28–34, Thames Street, Skinton
Description of works:	Six lock-up shops at ground level with eighteen flats over and basement car park and stores
Contract sum:	£495 000
Employer:	Skinton Development Co., High Path, Skinton
Main contractor:	Beecon Ltd., River Road, Skinton
Architect:	Draw & Partners, 25 Bridge Street, Skinton
Quantity surveyor:	Kewess & Partners, 52 High Street, Urbiston
Basis of contract:	JCT Standard Form of Contract, Private with Quantities, 1980 Edition with Amendments
Clauses from the Conditions of Contract not applicable:	22B, 22C
Entries on the Appendix to the Conditions of Contract:	*See* pp. 235–6
Commencing date:	21 March 1987
Completion date:	20 November 1988
Contract Period:	20 months

Abstract of information from Contract Bills

1. Amounts inserted in Bill No. 1 – Preliminaries

	£
Plant and scaffolding	4 500
Welfare facilities	3 600
Setting out the works	540
Foreman and supervision	20 000
Watching and lighting	1 350
Electric lighting and power	180
Temporary roads	1 350
Site huts	1 080
Site telephones	450
Site fencing and hoardings	1 620
Drying out building	450
Cleaning out	540
Total	35 660

2. P.c. sums and profit and attendance amounts included in Bill No. 5

	£	£
Nominated sub-contractors:		
Piling	11 700	
Profit 5%	585	
General attendance	270	
Other attendance	450	
Asphalt tanking and roofing	16 200	
Profit 5%	810	
General attendance	270	
Other attendance	180	
Electrical installation	18 000	
Profit 5%	900	
General attendance	450	
Other attendance	450	
Lifts installation	34 200	
Profit 5%	1 710	
General attendance	360	
Other attendance	720	
carried forward		87 255

		£	£
	brought forward		87 255
Nominated suppliers:			
Kitchen fitments		3 600	
Profit 5%		180	
Ironmongery		2 700	
Profit 5%		135	
Sanitary appliances		4 320	
Profit 5%		216	
			11 151
Statutory Bodies:			
Water main connection		360	
Profit 5%		18	
General attendance		–	
Electricity mains connection		360	
Profit 5%		18	
General attendance		–	
Gas main connection		540	
Profit 5%		27	
General attendance		–	
Sewer connection		900	
Profit 5%		45	
General attendance		–	
			2 268
Dayworks:			
Labour		1 500	
Additions to nett cost of labour 50%		750	
Materials		750	
Addition to nett cost of materials 20%		150	
Plant		750	
Addition to nett cost of plant 20%		150	
			4 050
Provisional Sums:			
Rates on temporary buildings		2 000	
Telephone for use of Employer		750	
Landscaping		2 250	
Contingencies		8 000	
			13 000
	Total		117 724

3. Summary of Bill No. 3

BILL NO. 3 – SHOPS AND FLATS

SUMMARY

PAGE		£
26	Excavation and earthwork	31 256.57
33	Concrete work	54 488.22
44	Brickwork and blockwork	45 417.33
69	Woodwork	55 342.64
75	Metalwork	9 468.72
89	Plumbing and mechanical engineering installations	27 475.76
92	Electrical installations	9 389.72
97	Floor, wall and ceiling finishings	22 100.50
102	Glazing	8 392.51
107	Painting and decorating	17 264.16
	TOTAL CARRIED TO GENERAL SUMMARY	280 596.13

108

4. General summary

GENERAL SUMMARY

PAGE		£
15	Bill No. 1 – Preliminaries	35 660.00
19	Bill No. 2 – Site clearance	5 531.00
108	Bill No. 3 – Shops and flats	280 596.13
143	Bill No. 4 – External works	40 556.51
147	Bill No. 5 – Prime cost sums and dayworks	117 724 00
		480 067.64

Add for:

	£
Insurance against injury to persons and property as item 5C	3 632.00
All Risks Insurance as item 5D	811.36
Water for the Works as item 13A	1 377.00
	485 888.00
Add to adjust for errors	9 112.00
TOTAL CARRIED TO FORM OF TENDER	495 000.00

148

5. List of basic prices of materials

Basic prices of materials

The contractor is required to enter below the materials and prices to which he wishes clauses 39.3 and 39.4 of the Conditions of the Contract to apply. Only materials, which are to be incorporated in the Works, are to be included in the list and the prices are to be those that have been used in the pricing of the bills of quantities. The contractor shall furnish to the architect, upon request, all suppliers' quotations and invoices in support of the prices on the list and of any claim based thereon.

Claims will be accepted only where they relate to fluctuations in the market price of any material included in the list. Claims will not be accepted which are based upon variations in price which are due to purchasing in small quantities or to materials being of a different quality from that specified in the bills of quantities.

Materials	Unit	Prices
Ordinary Portland cement	tonne	£ 51.04
Fletton bricks	1 000	£ 87.60
Sawn softwood – 25 × 50 mm	100 m	£ 24.05
38 × 100 mm	100 m	£ 69.55
50 × 150 mm	100 m	£123.50

Appendix B

Articles of Agreement

made the ___23rd___ day of ___February___ 19__87__

between ___A. Brown___

___

of (or whose registered office is situated at) ___Skinton___

___Development Company, High Path,___

___Skinton, Middlesex___

(hereinafter called 'the Employer') of the one part and

___J Green___

___

of (or whose registered office is situated at) ___Beacon Ltd___

___River Road, Skinton, Middlesex___

___

(hereinafter called 'the Contractor') (a) of the other part.

Whereas

Recitals   First   the Employer is desirous of (b) ___erecting a four - storey___ ___block of shops and flats___

(hereinafter called 'the Works') at

___28 - 34, Thames Street___

___Skinton, Middlesex___

and has caused Drawings and Bills of Quantities showing and describing the work to be done to be prepared by or under the direction of

___1. Draw R.I.B.A.___

Second   the Contractor has supplied the Employer with a fully priced copy of the said Bills of Quantities (which copy is hereinafter referred to as 'the Contract Bills');

Third   the said Drawings numbered _____ *462/1 to 462/23* _____

_____

(hereinafter referred to as 'the Contract Drawings') and the Contract Bills have been signed by or on behalf of the parties hereto;

Fourth   the status of the Employer, for the purposes of the statutory tax deduction scheme under the Finance (No. 2) Act, 1975, as at the Base Date is stated in the Appendix;

Now it is hereby agreed as follows

Contractor's obligations

Article 1
For the consideration hereinafter mentioned the Contractor will upon and subject to the Contract Documents carry out and complete the Works shown upon, described by or referred to in those Documents.

Contract sum

Article 2
The Employer will pay to the Contractor the sum of _____ *four hundred* _____

_____ *and ninety - five thousand pounds* _____

_____ (£ *495,000   00*)

(hereinafter referred to as 'the Contract Sum') or such other sum as shall become payable hereunder at the times and in the manner specified in the Conditions.

Architect

Article 3
The term 'the Architect' in the Conditions shall mean the said

_____ *I Draw R. I. B. A.* _____

of _____ *25 Bridge Street, Skinton,* _____

_____ *Middlesex* _____

or, in the event of his death or ceasing to be the Architect for the purpose of this Contract, such other person as the Employer shall nominate within a reasonable time but in any case no later than 21 days after such death or cessation for that purpose, not being a person to whom the Contractor no later than 7 days after such nomination shall object for reasons considered to be sufficient by an Arbitrator appointed in accordance with article 5. Provided always that no person subsequently appointed to be the Architect under this Contract shall be entitled to disregard or overrule any certificate or opinion or decision or approval or instruction given or expressed by the Architect for the time being.

_____

Footnotes   [c] Not used.   [d] Not used.

Appendix B

Quantity
Surveyor

Article 4
The Term 'the Quantity Surveyor' in the Conditions shall mean

C. Kewess F.R.I.C.S.

of _52 High Street, Umbiston, Survey_

or, in the event of his death or ceasing to be the Quantity Surveyor for the purpose of this Contract, such other person as the Employer shall nominate within a reasonable time but in any case no later than 21 days after such death or cessation for that purpose, not being a person to whom the Contractor no later than 7 days after such nomination shall object for reasons considered to be sufficient by an Arbitrator appointed in accordance with article 5.

Settlement of
disputes –
Arbitration

Article 5
If any dispute or difference as to the construction of this contract or any matter or thing of whatsoever nature arising thereunder or in connection therewith shall arise between the Employer or the Architect on his behalf and the Contractor either during the progress or after the completion or abandonment of the Works, except under clause 31 _(statutory tax deduction scheme)_ to the extent provided on clause 31·9 or under clause 3 of the VAT Agreement, it shall be and is hereby referred to arbitration in accordance with clause 41.

Footnotes   [e] Not used.   [f] Not used.

Signed by or on behalf of the Employer [g1] _____ *A Brown* _____

    in the presence of: *L Simpson*

Signed by or on behalf of the Contractor [g1] _____ *J. Green* _____

    in the presence of: *L Simpson*

Signed, sealed and delivered by [g2]/The common seal of [g3] : _____

    in the presence of [g2]/was hereunto affixed in the presence of [g3] :

Signed, sealed and delivered by [g2]/The common seal of [g3] : _____

    in the presence of [g2]/was hereunto affixed in the presence of [g3] :

Footnotes

[g1] For use if Agreement is executed under hand.

[g2] For use if executed under seal by an individual or firm or unincorporated body.

[g3] For use if executed under seal by a company or other body corporate.

Appendix

	Clause etc.	
Statutory tax deduction scheme – Finance (No. 2) Act 1975	Fourth recital and 31	Employer at Base Date *is a 'contractor'*/is not a 'contractor' for the purposes of the Act and the Regulations *(Delete as applicable)
Base Date	1·3	*2nd February 1987*
Date for completion	1·3	*20th November 1988*
Defects Liability Period (if none other stated is 6 months from the day named in the Certificate of Practical Completion of the Works)	17·2	
Assignment by Employer of benefits after Practical Completion	19·1·2	Clause 19·1·2 *applies*/does not apply *(Delete as applicable)
Insurance cover for any one occurrence or series of occurrences arising out of one event	21·1·1	£ *1,000,000*
Insurance – liability of Employer	21·2·1	Insurance *may be required*/is not required
		Amount of indemnity for any one occurrence or series of occurrences arising out of one event
		£_____ (y·1) *(Delete as applicable)
Insurance of the Works – alternative clauses	22·1	*Clause 22A/Clause 22B/ Clause 22C applies (See Footnote (m) to Clause 22) *(Delete as applicable)
Percentage to cover professional fees	*22A 22B·1 22C·2 *(Delete as applicable)	*Ten per cent*
Annual renewal date of insurance as supplied by Contractor	22A·3·1	*15th January*
Insurance for Employer's loss of liquidated damages – clause 25·4·3	22D	Insurance *may be required*/is not required *(Delete as applicable)
	22D·2	Period of time

	Clause etc.	
Date of Possession	23·1·1	*21st March 1987*
Deferment of the Date of Possession	23·1·2 25·4·13 26·1	Clause 23·1·2 *applies/does not apply Period of deferment if it is to be less than 6 weeks is
		* (Delete as applicable)
Liquidated and ascertained damages	24·2	at the rate of £ *1000* per *week*

It is essential that periods be inserted since otherwise no period of delay would be prescribed.

Period of delay: [z·1]	28·1·3	*one month*
Period of delay: [z·2]	28A·1·1 28A·1·3	*one month*
Period of delay: [z·3]	28A·1·2	*three months*
Period of Interim Certificates (if none stated is one month)	30·1·3	
Retention Percentage (if less than 5 per cent) [aa]	30·4·1·1	*three per cent*
Work reserved for Nominated Sub-Contractors for which the Contractor desires to tender	35·2	
Fluctuations: (if alternative required is not shown clause 38 shall apply)	37	~~clause 38~~ [cc] clause 39 ~~clause 40~~
Percentage addition	38·7 or 39·8	*ten per cent*
Formula Rules	40·1·1·1	
	rule 3	Base Month ———————— 19 ————
	rules 10 and 30 (i)	Part I/Part II [dd] of Section 2 of the Formula Rules is to apply
Settlement of disputes – Arbitration – appointor (if no appointor is selected the appointor shall be the President or a Vice-President, Royal Institute of British Architects)	41·1	President or a Vice-President: *Royal Institute of British Architects *Royal Institution of Chartered Surveyors *Chartered Institute of Arbitrators *(Delete as applicable)
Settlement of disputes – Arbitration	41·2	Clauses 41·2·1 and 41·2·2 apply (See clause 41·2·3)

Index to references to clauses in standard forms of contract

Subject index